AN EXAMPLES COURSE IN REACTION KINETICS

AN EXAMPLES COURSE IN REACTION KINETICS

An International Case Studies Approach

IAN M. CAMPBELL
Lecturer in Chemistry
University of Leeds

International Textbook Company

Blackie & Son Limited
Bishopbriggs
Glasgow G64 2NZ

Furnival House
14–18 High Holborn
London

First published 1980

International Standard Book Number
Hardback 0 7002 0275 7
Paperback 0 7002 0276 5

Typeset by CCC, printed and bound in
Great Britain by William Clowes (Beccles) Limited,
Beccles and London

PREFACE

The aim of this book is to present a progressive course of worked and exercise examples in chemical reaction kinetics. It is designed to complement lecture courses and the associated textbooks, and to cater for the importance attached currently to examples classes. My stimulus in producing this collection has been the belief that a comprehensive coverage of the subject by means of examples derived from recent literature constitutes a valuable teaching tool, and my experience in organising examples classes has been that students make obvious progress in their understanding of a course through the solution of carefully-chosen problems.

Surveying research papers in reaction kinetics, I have often found that comparatively simple theory is invoked, well within the understanding of students in chemically-orientated courses and often of direct relevance. My approach, based on research works from many countries, should convey the vitality of reaction kinetics, while also demonstrating that even a fairly elementary course has a relationship to current activity at the "frontiers of knowledge". It might be anticipated that the student would be sufficiently interested by a particular example to examine the original paper for details of the experimental technique, the thinking behind the research, or perhaps merely for an indication of the method of solution.

I have restricted my choice of source papers to those written in the English language and appearing in journals likely to be taken by higher education libraries. My hope is that the use of "real" sources of examples will augment and stimulate the interest of students of reaction kinetics within chemistry, chemical engineering, and biological and environmental sciences courses; some of the examples have been chosen with main disciplines other than chemistry in mind.

The teacher of reaction kinetics should find advantages beyond the obvious use in examples classes. Points of theory or experimental detail can be exemplified by reference to a worked example, where matters are developed straight-forwardly using familiar symbols—a procedure likely to appeal more to students than having to deal directly with references to research papers. A particular aspect of the course can be developed by collecting together relevant worked and exercise problems through the use of the keyword and back-referencing systems. The keywords (in bold, following the example number) have the main function of allowing the student, through the index of the course textbook, to refer to the appropriate basic theory; the back-referencing system leads the student to a worked example of relevance to the exercise problem. Further, the teacher may use the example and the quoted source to develop laboratory experiments and projects. The book also offers a sound basis for students to do examples work outside a formal class, so achieving broader coverage of the course content.

The actual numbers used in a problem statement are derived from the source paper, but only a few of the data are normally given. These are "improved" in the sense of removing random error, but the final result is that given in the source. Diagrams of straight-line plots are not shown, to avoid the waste of space entailed by a succession of them, but the data to be plotted are given directly so that the plot can be constructed easily if required.

Inevitably, through subjective preference or restriction of space, some of the aspects which could appear in reaction kinetics courses, particularly the more advanced ones, have been excluded. I have deliberately avoided areas involving complex mathematical or conceptual theory, such as detailed gas phase reaction dynamics (e.g. molecular beams, non-thermal-equilibrium reactants and products), modulation techniques, mixed solvent phenomena and solid state kinetics. However, I have introduced aspects of photochemical and electrochemical reaction kinetics, which are often neglected.

As the structure of the book is a progression through topics rather than levels of difficulty, the student should not be deterred by the early appearance of problems beyond his present level of understanding, but should look further into the worked examples for parts of examples which are within his scope. For instance, the Arrhenius equation is first introduced in example 5, but examples 21 and 26 also show its simple application within wider contexts. The index is designed to be helpful in locating other such cases.

When setting out on an exercise problem, the student should use the back-referencing numbers to check that it does not involve topics beyond his present level of understanding. However, many of the exercise problems are considerably less difficult than the worked examples to which they are referred. On occasions it should prove worthwhile for the student to tackle part of an exercise problem even if he considers that the rest is beyond his present ability.

I.M.C.
Leeds

CONTENTS

SECTION ONE

EXPERIMENTAL RATE LAWS AND THE DETERMINATION OF REACTION ORDERS AND RATE CONSTANTS

Example 1

Integrated first order rate law, gas burette.

The thermal decomposition of oxalic acid in a variety of solvents proceeds to completion according to the overall reaction equation:

$$(COOH)_2 \rightarrow CO_2 + HCOOH$$

The decomposition of 0·1606 g of oxalic acid in resorcinol (m-hydroxy phenol) as solvent has been followed by measurement of the volume (V) of carbon dioxide (CO_2), collected at a temperature of 300 K and a pressure of 101·3 kPa in a gas burette, as a function of time (t). With the solution maintained at a temperature of 398 K, the following values were obtained:

$10^2 V$ (dm^3)	0·421	0·921	1·458	2·220	2·992	3·425
t (s)	300	700	1200	2100	3400	4500

Show that the rate of decomposition is first order in oxalic acid and evaluate the rate constant at 398 K. (Assume that CO_2 is insoluble in resorcinol).

Source: Haleem, M. A. and Azeem, M. (1973) *Pakistan Journal of Scientific and Industrial Research*, **16**, p. 18. (Saudi Arabia)

Solution

Since the reaction has unit stoichiometry, the number of moles (n) of CO_2 collected must be equal to the number of moles of oxalic acid decomposed. If $V(\infty)$ is the volume of CO_2 which would be produced when all the oxalic acid is decomposed, then we have the relationship

$$\frac{V(\infty)}{V(\infty)-V} = \frac{C_0}{C}$$

where C_o is the initial concentration of oxalic acid and C is that at time t. The integrated first order rate law can then be expressed in the form

$$ {}_1kt = \ln\left(\frac{C_o}{C}\right) = \ln V(\infty) - \ln(V(\infty) - V) $$

where ${}_1k$ is the first order rate constant. Hence a plot of $\ln(V(\infty) - V)$ versus t should be linear for first order kinetics, with a gradient of $-{}_1k$.

We must first calculate the value of $V(\infty)$ from the initial mass of oxalic acid added: this is given as 0·1606 g and, since the relative molecular mass of oxalic acid is $2 \times (12 + 16 + 16 + 1) = 90$, the number of moles present initially is $n = 1{\cdot}784 \times 10^{-3}$. Application of the ideal gas law for pressure $P = 1{\cdot}013 \times 10^5$ Pa and temperature $T = 300$ K yields

$$ V(\infty) = \frac{nRT}{P} = \frac{1{\cdot}784 \times 10^{-3} \times 8{\cdot}314 \times 300}{1{\cdot}013 \times 10^5} $$
$$ = 0{\cdot}0439 \text{ dm}^3 $$

Hence the data for the plot are as follows:

$10^2(V(\infty) - V)$ (dm^3)	3·97	3·47	2·94	2·17	1·40	0·965
$\ln 10^2(V(\infty) - V)$	1·379	1·244	1·077	0·775	0·336	−0·0356
t (s)	300	700	1200	2100	3400	4500

The plot is accurately linear with gradient of $-3{\cdot}36 \times 10^{-4}$ s^{-1}. Thus the first order rate law holds and ${}_1k = 3{\cdot}36 \times 10^{-4}$ s^{-1} at 398 K. (For the application of the integrated first order rate law to a gas phase reaction see examples 6 and 26.)

Example 2

Integrated second order rate laws (unity stoichiometry), pseudo-order rate law.

The reaction between p-bromophenylchloroformate (ArOCOCl) and (silver) nitrate to yield 2-nitro-4-bromophenol with unity stoichiometry has been studied in acetonitrile solution at 294 K. The rate of consumption of ArOCOCl was determined by measuring the rate of disappearance of the chloroformate carbonyl peak in the infrared so that a profile of its concentration (C) versus time (t) was obtained.

With equal initial concentrations of 0·115 mol dm^{-3} of both reactants, the results were as follows:

10^2C (mol dm^{-3})	8·21	6·38	4·79	3·66
$10^{-3}t$ (s)	0·600	1·200	2·100	3·200

In another experiment with the same initial value of C but with an initial concentration of nitrate of 0·585 mol dm^{-3} the results were as follows:

10^2C (mol dm^{-3})	8·23	5·98	3·26	0·584
$10^{-2}t$ (s)	1·00	2·00	4·00	10·00

Show that these results are consistent with an initial bimolecular step, $ArOCOCl + NO_3^-$, being rate-determining in both experiments, using an exact second order rate law analysis and evaluating the second order rate constant. Apply a pseudo-first order rate law analysis to the second set of results and compare the rate constant values obtained by the two analyses.
Source: Zabik, M. J. and Schuetz, R. D. (1967) *Journal of Organic Chemistry*, **32**, p. 300. (U.S.A.)

Solution
The initial reaction step is to be regarded as

$$ArOCOCl + NO_3^- \rightarrow \text{products}$$

and the overall reaction has a unity stoichiometry. Such a bimolecular reaction will obey second order kinetics and, if this is the rate-determining step, this will be imposed upon the observed overall rate.

For the first set of results where the initial concentrations are equal, the integrated second order rate law applicable will be of the form

$$C^{-1} - C_o^{-1} = {}_2kt$$

where C_o is the initial concentration of ArOCOCl and C is that at time t and ${}_2k$ is the second order rate constant. Thus we plot C^{-1} versus t, when a linear plot should result with gradient ${}_2k$. The data for the plot are as follows:

C^{-1} (dm^3 mol^{-1})	8·70	12·2	15·7	20·9	27·3
t (s)	0	600	1200	2100	3200

The plot is linear as required with gradient of $5{\cdot}90 \times 10^{-3}$ dm^3 mol^{-1} s^{-1} = ${}_2k$.

In the second set of data the initial concentrations are not equal so that the exact second order rate law in integrated form will be

$$ {}_2kt = (b-a)^{-1} \ln\left(\frac{a(b-x)}{b(a-x)}\right) \qquad (b > a) \qquad \text{(i)}$$

where b is the initial concentration of NO_3^-, a is the initial concentration of ArOCOCl and x is the concentration of each reactant removed in time t. Thus $b = 0{\cdot}585$ mol dm^{-3}, $a = 0{\cdot}115$ mol dm^{-3} and $C = a - x$. One approach to proving the validity of equation (i) here is to use it to calculate a set of values of ${}_2k$ for each C, which should be constant. The progression of the calculation is as follows:

$10^2(a-x)$(mol dm^{-3})	8·23	5·98	3·26	0·584
$10^2(b-x)$(mol dm^{-3})	55·2	53·0	50·3	47·5
$\ln\{a(b-x)/b(a-x)\}$	0·277	0·555	1·109	2·774
$10^3\,{}_2k$ (dm^3 mol^{-1} s^{-1})	5·89	5·90	5·90	5·90

These values are effectively constant and identical with the value of ${}_2k$ derived from the first set of results, indicating the same rate-determining step.

The second order rate law in differential form is

$$-\frac{dC}{dt} = {}_2kC[NO_3^-]$$

If in the second experiment we regard $[NO_3^-]$ as being large enough with respect to C to be considered as invariant, then we derive the pseudo-first order rate law in differential form

$$-\frac{dC}{dt} = {}_1kC \qquad \text{(ii)}$$

with ${}_1k = {}_2k[NO_3^-]$. However from the values of $(b-x)$ given above, we can see that it is not strictly correct to regard $[NO_3^-]$ as invariant, so that it might be advisable to use the average value of $[NO_3^-]$ equal to 0·53 mol dm^{-3}. The integrated form of equation (ii) is the integrated first order form

$$\ln\left(\frac{C_o}{C}\right) = {}_1kt$$

and $-{}_1k$ is the predicted gradient of a linear plot of $\ln C$ versus t. The data for the plot derived from the second set of results are as follows:

$\ln C$	−2·163	−2·497	−2·817	−3·423	−5·143
t (s)	0	100	200	400	1000

The plot shows slight curvature (reflecting significant consumption of NO_3^-) but in an actual experiment this would be likely to be masked by random errors. The average gradient yields ${}_1k = 2{\cdot}98 \times 10^{-3}$ s^{-1} and hence by dividing by the average $[NO_3^-]$ we obtain ${}_2k = 5{\cdot}64 \times 10^{-3}$ dm^3 mol^{-1} s^{-1}. This result is evidently close to the exact analysis values above but the difference reflects the approximation of the pseudo-first order approach. It is then clear that we must regard an initial concentration ratio of greater than the 5 used here as being required for application of a pseudo-first order rate law with tolerable accuracy.

(For a further instance of the application of pseudo-order rate laws, see examples 4, 5 and 11).

Example 3

Integrated second order rate law (non-unity stoichiometry), conventional rate constant.

Ammonium metavanadate dissolved in strong acid provides a solution of vanadium (V) (V(V)) which reacts with dissolved arsenious oxide (As_2O_3) according to the overall stoichiometric equation

$$As_2O_3 + 4V(V) + 2H_2O \rightarrow As_2O_5 + 4V(IV) + 4H^+$$

The following concentration profile as a function of time (t) was obtained in an experiment conducted at 318 K in 4M H_2SO_4 with an initial concentration of As_2O_3 of $1{\cdot}056 \times 10^{-2}$ mol dm^{-3}:

10^2[V(V)] (mol dm^{-3})	2·00	1·68	1·17	0·98	0·75	0·61	0·47
t (min)	0	14·92	49·55	68·22	98·35	123·1	155·9

Show that these data conform to a reaction first order in each of V(V) and As_2O_3 and calculate the value of the conventional rate constant at 318 K.
Source: Pal, B. B., Mukherjee, D. C. and Sengupta, K. K. (1971) *Journal of Inorganic and Nuclear Chemistry*, **34**, p. 3433. (India)

Solution
Let a represent the initial concentration of As_2O_3 and b represent that of V(V). Let x represent the concentration of V(V) reacted at time t. If the reaction is first order in both reactants, then the conventional, overall second order rate law in differential form will be

$$-\frac{\frac{1}{4}d[\mathrm{V(V)}]}{dt} = {}_2k[\mathrm{As_2O_3}][\mathrm{V(V)}]$$

i.e.
$$-\frac{\frac{1}{4}d(b-x)}{dt} = \frac{\frac{1}{4}dx}{dt} = {}_2k(a-\tfrac{1}{4}x)(b-x)$$

where ${}_2k$ is the conventional second order rate constant. The integrated form of this equation is

$${}_2k = t^{-1}(4a-b)^{-1}\ln\left(\frac{b(4a-x)}{4a(b-x)}\right)$$

Thus since ${}_2k$ should be a constant if the reaction is second order, then if we calculate values of $\ln\{b(4a-x)/4a(b-x)\}$ for the data given and plot them versus the corresponding values of t, we should obtain a linear plot passing through the origin with gradient equal to $(4a-b)_2k$. The data for the plot are given below:

10^2x (mol dm^{-3})	0·32	0·83	1·02	1·25	1·39	1·53
$\ln\{b(4a-x)/4a(b-x)\}$	0·0956	0·317	0·437	0·630	0·788	0·998
t (min)	14·92	49·55	68·22	98·35	123·1	155·9

The plot is linear and passes through the origin as required, showing that the data given conform to a reaction first order in each reactant. The gradient of the plot is

$$6{\cdot}44\times10^{-3}\ \text{min}^{-1} = {}_2k\{(4\times1{\cdot}056\times10^{-2})-2{\cdot}00\times10^{-2}\} = 2{\cdot}22\times10^{-2}\ {}_2k.$$

Hence $\quad {}_2k = 0{\cdot}290\ \text{dm}^3\ \text{mol}^{-1}\ \text{min}^{-1}$ or $4{\cdot}83\times10^{-3}\ \text{dm}^3\ \text{mol}^{-1}\ \text{s}^{-1}$.

Example 4

Initial rates method, rate constant units, general form of integrated rate law, isolation method, conventional rate law.

The rate of the reaction between iodate and iodide has been measured in aqueous solutions of constant ionic strength and pH, with the extent of reaction monitored by the amount of strong acid added to maintain the pH. The stoichiometric equation for the overall reaction is

$$IO_3^- + 8I^- + 6H^+ \rightarrow 3I_3^- + 3H_2O$$

The initial rates of IO_3^- consumption (R_i) were derived as follows at 298 K and pH = 6·70:

Experiment number	1	2	3	4	5
$10^2[IO_3^-]$ (mol dm^{-3})	3·8	4·5	5·0	3·8	4·5
$10^2[I^-]$ (mol dm^{-3})	3·0	3·0	3·6	5·0	7·0
10^8R_i (mol dm^{-3} s^{-1})	0·84	1·17	3·00	6·46	34·8

Evaluate the partial orders of the reaction and the conventional rate constant at 298 K.

If $[IO_3^-]$ was made very much larger than $[I^-]$, what function of the latter would be expected to yield a linear plot against time, on the assumption that the reaction mechanism was the same? How would the gradient of this plot be related to the rate constant calculated from the initial rate data above?

Source: Barton, A. F. M., Cheong, H. N. and Smidt, R. E. (1976) *Journal of the Chemical Society, Faraday Transactions I*, **72**, p. 568. (New Zealand)

Solution

The initial rate law will be expressed as

$$R_i = {}_nk[IO_3^-]^p[I^-]^q$$

where the partial orders are p and q and $n=p+q$ is the overall order, with the concentrations being the initial ones.

We note that experiments 1 and 2 have the same $[I^-]$, so that R_i will be proportional simply to $[IO_3^-]^p$. Taking logarithms we therefore derive

$$\ln R_i = \text{constant} + p \ln [IO_3^-]$$

i.e.
$$\frac{\Delta \ln R_i}{\Delta \ln [IO_3^-]} = p$$

In experiment 1, for $10^8 R_i = 0{\cdot}84$, ln $0{\cdot}84 = -0{\cdot}1744$ and $\ln 10^2[IO_3^-] = 1{\cdot}3350$. In experiment 2, for $10^8 R_i = 1{\cdot}17$, ln $1{\cdot}17 = 0{\cdot}1570$ and $\ln 10^2[IO_3^-] = 1{\cdot}5041$. Hence $p = 0{\cdot}3314/0{\cdot}1691 = 1{\cdot}96 \simeq 2$ (we may expect an integer value on the basis of such small deviation).

Also experiments 1 and 4 have the same $[IO_3^-]$ so that $R_i \propto [I^-]^q$ and hence

$$\frac{\Delta \ln R_i}{\Delta \ln [I^-]} = q$$

In experiment 1, for $10^8 R_i = 0{\cdot}84$, $\ln 0{\cdot}84 = -0{\cdot}1744$ and $\ln 10^2[I^-] = 1{\cdot}0986$. In experiment 4, for $10^8 R_i = 6{\cdot}46$, $\ln 6{\cdot}46 = 1{\cdot}8656$ and $\ln 10^2[I^-] = 1{\cdot}6094$. Hence $q = 2{\cdot}0400/0{\cdot}5108 = 3{\cdot}99 \simeq 4$.

If we are correct in taking $p = 2$ and $q = 4$, then for all the experiments the ratio $R_i/[I^-]^4[IO_3^-]^2$ should be constant. The values are as follows:

Experiment number	1	2	3	4	5
$R_i/[I^-]^4[IO_3^-]^2$ ($mol^{-5}\,dm^{15}\,s^{-1}$)	7·18	7·13	7·14	7·16	7·16

These values are evidently close enough to constancy to justify the rate law

$$R_i = 7{\cdot}2[IO_3^-]^2[I^-]^4 \text{ mol dm}^{-3}\,\text{s}^{-1}$$

The rate constant will have sixth order units, i.e. $n = 6$ in the general formula $dm^{3(n-1)}\,mol^{(1-n)}\,s^{-1}$, and the conventional rate constant is ${}_6k = 7{\cdot}2\ dm^{15}\,mol^{-5}\,s^{-1}$ since R_i is defined as $-d[IO_3^-]/dt$ and iodate has a unity stoichiometry in the overall equation.

The second part of the question refers to the reaction when it is allowed to proceed to a significant extent and represents an application of the *isolation method* for determining a partial reaction order. Since the concentration of IO_3^- is very large compared to $[I^-]$, it can be considered as constant and the conventional rate law can be reduced to the pseudo-fourth order form

$$-\frac{\frac{1}{8}\,d[I^-]}{dt} = {}_4k[I^-]^4$$

where ${}_4k = {}_6k[IO_3^-]^2$. The integrated form of the general q^{th} order rate law $-dC/dt = {}_qkC^q$ is

$$(q-1)^{-1}C^{(1-q)} = {}_qkt + \text{constant}$$

Hence with $q=4$, we should expect a plot of the reciprocal of $[I^-]^3$ versus time to be linear, and on inserting the stoichiometry number of 8 as demanded by the conventional rate law, we expect the equation to hold

$$\tfrac{1}{3}[I^-]^{-3} = 8_4kt + \text{constant}$$

Thus the plot of $[I^-]^{-3}$ versus t will have a gradient of $24_4k = 24_6k[IO_3^-]^2$.

Note: The integrated rate law forms for a fractional order reaction can be developed from the general equation given above: for exemplification see example 37.

Example 5

Half-life method, pseudo-order rate law, Arrhenius equation, activation energy.

The reaction of ozone with ethanol in carbon tetrachloride solution has been studied using spectrophotometry to measure the time ($t_{1/2}$) taken for one half of the initial ozone concentration to disappear. The table below shows values of $t_{1/2}$ (s) as a function of initial concentrations of reactants at 298 K, while the figures given in brackets are the corresponding $t_{1/2}$ (s) for temperatures of 308 K and 318 K respectively:

$10^4[O_3]_o$ (mol dm^{-3})	$[C_2H_5OH]$ (mol dm^{-3})			
	0·009	0·014	0·020	0·025
1·1 } 3·5 }	220 (136, 86)	141	99 (61, 39)	79

Deduce the partial orders of the reaction and the Arrhenius equation for the rate constant concerned.

Source: Gerchikov, A. Ya., Kuznetsova, E. P. and Denisov, E. T. (1974) *Kinetics and Catalysis* (English translation of *Kinetika i Kataliz*), **15**, p. 446 (U.S.S.R.)

Solution

The data given are the half lives for ozone consumption. We note that the ethanol concentrations are around two orders of magnitude greater than those of ozone so that we may apply the pseudo-order rate law

$$-\frac{d[O_3]}{dt} = {}_nk[O_3]^p[C_2H_5OH]^q \simeq {}_pk[O_3]^p$$

where ${}_nk$ is the overall rate constant for the nth order reaction ($n=p+q$) and ${}_pk$ is the pseudo-p^{th} order rate constant, equal to ${}_nk[C_2H_5OH]^q$.

We see immediately that $t_{1/2}$ is independent of $[O_3]_o$, which indicates $p=1$ since for a first order reaction

$$t_{1/2} = \frac{\ln 2}{{}_1k}$$

Hence here we have the relationship

$$t_{1/2} = \frac{0{\cdot}693}{{}_nk[C_2H_5OH]^q}$$

We can evaluate q by plotting $\ln t_{1/2}$ versus $\ln[C_2H_5OH]$, since from the above equation, on taking logarithms

$$\ln t_{1/2} = \text{constant} - q \ln[C_2H_5OH]$$

The data for the plot (for 298 K) are as follows:

$\ln[C_2H_5OH]$	$-4{\cdot}711$	$-4{\cdot}269$	$-3{\cdot}912$	$-3{\cdot}689$
$\ln t_{1/2}$	5·394	4·949	4·595	4·369

The plot has a gradient of -1 so that $q=1$. Thus $n=p+q=1+1$ and the reaction is second order overall.

The ratios of the half-lives at the different temperatures can be expressed with $t_{1/2}$ at 298 K as numerator for corresponding concentrations of C_2H_5OH:

T (K)	$[C_2H_5OH]$ (mol dm^{-3})	
	0·009	0·020
308	1·62	1·62
318	2·56	2·54

Within likely experimental error, these values confirm that the order does not vary in the temperature range 298 to 318 K. Also since $t_{1/2}$ is inversely proportional to ${}_2k$ and if

$${}_2k = A \exp \frac{-E_a}{RT}$$

as the Arrhenius equation with A designated as the pre-exponential factor and E_a as the apparent Arrhenius activation energy, then a plot of the logarithm of the average value of the half-life ratios (1·00 at 298 K, 1·62 at 308 K and 2·55 at 318 K) versus K/T should be linear with gradient of $-E_a/R$. The data for the plot are:

T (K)	298	308	318
10^3 K/T	3·356	3·247	3·145
ln (ratio)	0	0·4824	0·9361

The plot is close to linear with an average gradient of $-4{\cdot}5 \times 10^3$ K$=-E_a/R$, so that $E_a = 37$ kJ mol^{-1}.

To evaluate the Arrhenius equation A factor, we must calculate the value of ${}_2k$ at 298 K. A plot of $t_{1/2}$ versus $[C_2H_5OH]^{-1}$ is expected to be linear with gradient of $0{\cdot}693/_2k$ on the basis of a relationship developed above with insertion of $n=2$ and $q=1$. The data for this plot are as follows:

$t_{1/2}$ (s)	220	141	99	79
$[C_2H_5OH]^{-1}$ ($dm^3\ mol^{-1}$)	111	71	50	40

The gradient is $1{\cdot}96\ mol\ dm^{-3}\ s=0{\cdot}693/_2k$, so that $_2k=0{\cdot}354\ dm^3\ mol^{-1}\ s^{-1}$ at 298 K. Equating this to $A\exp(-37\times10^3/8{\cdot}314\times298)$ yields the value $A=1{\cdot}1\times10^6\ dm^3\ mol^{-1}\ s^{-1}$.
(See example 25 for the half-life of a reaction following second order kinetics)

Example 6

Stirred-flow (backmix) reactor, linear-flow reactor (plug-flow), integrated first order rate law, surface to volume ratio, gas chromatography

The gas phase thermal decomposition of $C(NF_2)_4$ at large dilution in helium has been studied in a stirred-flow and a tubular reactor in separate experiments at 505 K. The spherical stirred-flow reactor had an internal volume of $9{\cdot}5\times10^{-2}\ dm^3$ and the volume flow rate (U) through it was measured at 300 K at the operating pressure. Gas chromatographic analysis was used to measure the ratio (F) of the concentration of $C(NF_2)_4$ at the reactor exit to that at the reactor entry for a set of values of U within the stirred-flow operation regime, and the results were as follows:

10^4U ($dm^3\ s^{-1}$)	104	37·3	20·7	8·90
F	0·775	0·554	0·408	0·228

The tubular reactor was 36·6 dm of uniform tubing of internal diameter 4·57 mm and values of F as a function of U in this case were as follows, for operation in the plug flow regime with insignificant pressure gradient:

10^4U ($dm^3\ s^{-1}$)	48·8	28·1	16·4	11·5
F	0·675	0·506	0·310	0·189

Show that both sets of results correspond to a first order decomposition of $C(NF_2)_4$. Calculate the rate constants for decomposition and the surface to volume ratio for both reactors and hence specify whether the reaction is homogeneous, heterogeneous or of mixed nature.
Source: Sullivan, J. M., Axworthy, A. E. and Houser, J. T. (1970) *Journal of Physical Chemistry*, **74**, p. 2611. (U.S.A.)

Solution
For a single reactant decomposing in a stirred-flow reactor with first order kinetics and at large dilution in an inert gas, the differential form of the rate law takes the form

$$\frac{dN}{dt} = C_0U - CU - {}_1kCV = 0 \tag{i}$$

where N is the number of moles of reactant in the reactor, C_0 and C are the concentrations of the reactant in the entry flow and in the reactor (and in the exit flow) respectively, U is the volume flow rate at the reactor temperature, V is the volume of the reactor and ${}_1k$ is the first order rate constant. The average residence time in the reactor is defined as

$$\tau_R = V/U$$

and there is complete mixing, i.e. uniform concentrations by definition in the reactor. On rearrangement, equation (i) becomes

$$\frac{\Delta C}{C} = \frac{C_0 - C}{C}$$
$$= {}_1k\tau_R$$

With F defined as C/C_0 this yields the relationship

$$F^{-1} - 1 = {}_1k\tau_R$$

Hence a plot of F^{-1} versus τ_R should be linear with a gradient of ${}_1k$. We note that U is specified for 300 K as opposed to the reactor temperature of 505 K, so that in terms of the values given, τ_R is defined as

$$\tau_R = \frac{V300}{U505} = 5{\cdot}64 \times \frac{10^{-2}}{U\,\text{dm}^{-3}}$$

The data for the plot for the stirred-flow reactor are:

F^{-1}	1·29	1·81	2·45	4·39
τ_R (s)	5·43	15·0	27·1	62·9

The plot is linear with gradient ${}_1k = 0{\cdot}054\ \text{s}^{-1}$, demonstrating the first order behaviour. Also the intercept is 1·0 as required.

In the tubular reactor, the first order decay equation in integrated form will be

$$\ln\left(\frac{C_0}{C}\right) = {}_1kt$$

where C_0 is the concentration of reactant at entry and C is that at a flowtime t downstream from the point of entry. A tubular reactor of internal diameter $4{\cdot}57 \times 10^{-2}$ dm and length 36·6 dm has a volume of $\pi(2{\cdot}29 \times 10^{-2})^2 36{\cdot}6 = 0{\cdot}602\ \text{dm}^3$. The flowtime t is defined in the same way as τ_R above, and in terms of the given values $t = V300/U505 = 3{\cdot}58 \times 10^{-2}/U\,\text{dm}^{-3}$. Hence in this case, since $F = C/C_0$, a plot of $\ln(F^{-1})$ versus t should be linear, pass through the origin and have gradient of ${}_1k$. The data for the plot are as follows:

$\ln(F^{-1})$	0·393	0·681	1·171	1·666
t (s)	7·34	12·7	21·8	31·1

The plot is linear, passes through the origin and has gradient ${}_1k=0{\cdot}054\ \mathrm{s}^{-1}$.

The volume of a spherical reactor is

$$V=\tfrac{4}{3}\pi r^3$$

and the surface area is

$$S=4\pi r^2$$

where r is the radius. For $V=9{\cdot}5\times10^{-2}\ \mathrm{dm}^3$, $r=0{\cdot}283$ dm and $S=1{\cdot}01\ \mathrm{dm}^2$, so that $S/V=10{\cdot}6\ \mathrm{dm}^{-1}$. For the tubular reactor

$$S=2\pi rl$$

and

$$V=\pi r^2 l$$

where l is the length, and $S/V=2/r=87{\cdot}5\ \mathrm{dm}^{-1}$. Now, if part of the reaction is proceeding heterogeneously on the walls, that component will have a rate dependent on S for the reactor, while that part occurring in the gas phase will depend upon V. Hence we should expect ${}_1k$ (defined with respect to unit volume through the use of concentrations) to be expressible as

$${}_1k=k_\mathrm{g}+k_\mathrm{s}\left(\frac{S}{V}\right)$$

where k_g is the gas phase rate constant and k_s is an effective heterogeneous rate constant. The observed fact that changing the S/V ratio by nearly a factor of 8 from the stirred-flow to the tubular reactor does not alter the value of ${}_1k$ means that the reaction must be regarded as entirely homogeneous.

SECTION TWO

NEAR-EQUILIBRIUM KINETICS

Example 7

Integrated rate law for reversible second order reaction, Principle of Microscopic Reversibility and Detailed Balancing, integrated second order rate law (unity stoichiometry), pseudo-order reaction, stopped-flow method.

The reversible elementary reaction between nitrosyl chloride (NOCl) and n-butanol (ROH) to form n-butyl nitrite (RONO) and HCl has been studied in glacial acetic acid solution at 293 K using a stopped-flow system, the absorbance of NOCl at a wavelength of 464 nm being used to establish its concentration as a function of time (t). When the initial concentrations were $2{\cdot}00 \times 10^{-2}$ mol dm^{-3} (NOCl) and $1{\cdot}50$ mol dm^{-3} (ROH), the results were:

10^2[NOCl] (mol dm^{-3})	1·63	1·41	1·06	0·830	0·570
$10^3 t$ (s)	1·64	2·84	5·50	8·46	∞

Calculate the values of the forward and reverse rate constants at 293 K.

In a separate experiment, starting with [RONO]=[HCl]=$2{\cdot}00 \times 10^{-2}$ mol dm^{-3}, [NOCl] was measured as a function of time as follows:

10^2[NOCl] (mol dm^{-3})	0·256	0·519	0·706
$10^3 t$ (s)	2·10	5·00	7·80

Show that the rate of reaction in this latter experiment is consistent with that indicated by the first experiment and comment on the application of the Principle of Microscopic Reversibility and Detailed Balancing to this system.
Source: Dalcq, A. and Bruylants, A. (1975) *Tetrahedron Letters*, **6**, p. 377. (Belgium)

Solution
The reaction system may be represented as

$$ROH + NOCl \underset{k_b}{\overset{k_f}{\rightleftharpoons}} RONO + HCl$$

where k_f and k_b are the forward and reverse rate constants respectively. We note that the starting conditions in the first experiment are pseudo-first order since $[ROH] \gg [NOCl]$, so that we may define a pseudo-first order rate constant, ${}_1k = k_f[ROH]$. Let the initial concentration of NOCl be a, that at time t be $a-x$ and that at equilibrium ($t=\infty$) be $a-x_e$. The product concentrations will both be x at time t and x_e at equilibrium from the stoichiometry. The differential form of the rate law will then be:

$$-\frac{d(a-x)}{dt} = \frac{dx}{dt} = {}_1k(a-x) - k_b x^2$$

At equilibrium the rates of the forward and reverse reaction are equal, i.e. we have ${}_1k(a-x_e) = k_b x_e^2$ and using this to substitute for k_b we derive:

$$\frac{dx}{dt} = {}_1k(a-x) - \frac{{}_1k(a-x_e)x^2}{x_e^2}$$

$$= \frac{{}_1k}{x_e^2}(x_e - x)(ax_e + (a-x_e)x)$$

Collecting variables, splitting into partial fractions and integrating we have

$$\int_0^x \frac{dx}{(x_e-x)(ax_e+(a-x_e)x)} = \int_0^x \frac{A\,dx}{(x_e-x)} + \int_0^x \frac{B\,dx}{(ax_e+(a-x_e)x)}$$

$$= -A \ln\left(\frac{x_e - x}{x_e}\right) + \frac{B}{a-x_e} \ln\left(\frac{ax_e+(a-x_e)x}{ax_e}\right)$$

$$= \frac{{}_1k}{x_e^2}\int_0^t dt$$

$$= \frac{{}_1k}{x_e^2}t$$

The partial fractionation process involves the equation

$$Aax_e + A(a-x_e)x + Bx_e - Bx = 1$$

(true for all x), so that the only solution is represented by the equations

$$Aax_e + Bx_e = 1$$

$$A(a-x_e) - B = 0$$

The solutions derived are $A = (2ax_e - x_e^2)^{-1}$ and $B = (a-x_e)/(2ax_e - x_e^2)$. Upon insertion of these values into the integrated equation above, and taking out the common factor with combination of the logarithmic terms, we obtain

$$_1kt = \frac{x_e}{2a - x_e} \ln\left(\frac{ax_e + (a - x_e)x}{a(x_e - x)}\right)$$

We may now apply this equation to the given data for the first experiment, when $a = 2{\cdot}00 \times 10^{-2}$ mol dm^{-3}, $x_e = (2{\cdot}00 - 0{\cdot}570) \times 10^{-2} = 1{\cdot}43 \times 10^{-2}$ mol dm^{-3} and the concentrations listed are $a - x$. Hence we calculate a set of values of $_1kt$ listed below:

10^2x (mol dm^{-3})	0·37	0·59	0·94	1·17
$_1kt$	0·206	0·358	0·691	1·065
10^3t (s)	1·64	2·84	5·50	8·46
$_1k$ (s^{-1})	126	126	126	126

Since $_1k = 126$ s^{-1} when [ROH] = 1·50 mol dm^{-3}, $k_f = 126/1{\cdot}50 = 84{\cdot}0$ dm^3 mol^{-1} s^{-1}. Also, from the equilibrium composition

$$k_b = \frac{_1k(a - x_e)}{x_e^2} = \frac{126 \times 5{\cdot}7 \times 10^{-3}}{(1{\cdot}43 \times 10^{-2})^2} = 3{\cdot}51 \times 10^3 \text{ dm}^3 \text{ mol}^{-1} \text{ s}^{-1}$$

In view of the fact that $k_b \gg k_f$ and the extent of reaction is not large, we can analyse the second set of data as a straightforward second order reaction without incurring significant error. Letting C be the concentration of RONO and HCl at time t, the integrated rate law will be

$$C^{-1} - C_o^{-1} = k_b t$$

where C_o is the initial concentration. Therefore a plot of C^{-1} versus t should be a straight line of gradient k_b. The data for the plot are:

C^{-1} (dm^3 mol^{-1})	50·0	57·3	67·5	77·3
10^3t (s)	0	2·10	5·00	7·80

The plot is linear as required and has gradient of $3{\cdot}51 \times 10^3$ dm^3 mol^{-1} s^{-1} $= k_b$.

Thus the values of k_b from the two experiments are identical. It is the Principle of Microscopic Reversibility and Detailed Balancing which allows the equation of the ratio k_f/k_b to the equilibrium constant, which is confirmed by the isolated value of k_b from the second experiment matching that derived from the first experiment. We may also note that this provides evidence that reaction rate constants preserve the same values under conditions far from equilibrium as pertain at equilibrium.

Example 8

Temperature jump system, integrated rate law for a relaxation system, characteristic relaxation time, optical density or absorbance, Beer-Lambert law.

When a temperature jump (5–10 K) experiment was performed on an aqueous haemoglobin (Hb) solution containing dissolved oxygen, the displacement of the optical density (ΔA) of Hb at 366 nm from its final equilibrium value was measured as a function of time (t). For a solution relaxing at 298 K with $[\text{Hb}]+[\text{O}_2]=5{\cdot}3\times10^{-6}$ mol dm^{-3}, the following set of values was obtained:

ΔA (arbitrary units)	5·87	5·17	4·63	4·20	3·87	2·88	2·33	1·93	1·61	1·34
t (ms)	1	2	3	4	5	10	15	20	25	30

Show that two relaxation processes are occurring and obtain the characteristic relaxation times for the fast (τ_F) and slow (τ_S) components of the decay.

The slower process corresponds to the relaxation of the equilibrium

$$\text{Hb}+\text{O}_2 \rightleftharpoons \text{HbO}_2$$

and further values of τ_S as a function of $[\text{Hb}]+[\text{O}_2]$ were obtained as follows under the same conditions:

τ_S (ms)	11·2	7·86	5·43
$10^5([\text{Hb}]+[\text{O}_2])$ (mol dm^{-3})	2·5	3·9	6·0

Calculate the values of the forward and reverse reaction rate constants.

Source: Brunori, M. and Schuster, T. M. (1969) *Journal of Biological Chemistry*, **244**, pps. 4, 46. (Italy)

Solution

Optical density (absorbance) is defined as

$$A = \log_{10}\frac{I_0}{I_t} = \varepsilon Cl$$

according to the form of the Beer-Lambert law, where I_0 is the incident intensity of the radiation, I_t is the transmitted intensity, ε is termed the decadic absorption (extinction) coefficient, C is the concentration of the absorbing species in the medium and l is the path-length through the medium. It follows that, for all the other parameters constant, $\Delta A \propto \Delta C$, where ΔA is the displacement of optical density and ΔC is the displacement in the concentration of Hb (the only absorber at 366 nm) from the final equilibrium values.

The integrated rate law for a relaxation involving a single equilibrium has the form

$$\ln \frac{\Delta C_0}{\Delta C} = \ln \frac{\Delta A_0}{\Delta A} = \frac{t}{\tau}$$

where ΔC_0 is the concentration displacement at $t=0$ (i.e. before the temperature jump was applied) corresponding to the displacement ΔA_0 in optical density and τ is the characteristic relaxation time.

For two relaxation processes characterised by τ_F and τ_S, the total optical density displacement at time t can be expressed as the sum

$$\Delta A = A_F \exp\left(\frac{-t}{\tau_F}\right) + A_S \exp\left(\frac{-t}{\tau_S}\right)$$

where A_F and A_S are the zero time displacements of optical density resulting from the displacement of two separate equilibria. If $\tau_F \ll \tau_S$, then as t becomes relatively large, $\Delta A \rightarrow A_S \exp(-t/\tau_S)$ and

$$\ln \Delta A \rightarrow \ln A_S - \frac{t}{\tau_S}$$

Under these circumstances a plot of $\ln \Delta A$ versus t should tend towards a straight line of gradient $= -\tau_S^{-1}$ at larger t. The data to be plotted are:

$\ln \Delta A$	1·770	1·643	1·533	1·435	1·353	1·058	0·846	0·658	0·476	0·293
$10^3 t$ (s)	1	2	3	4	5	10	15	20	25	30

The plot is shown in figure 2.1. The last three points lie on a straight line of gradient $-36{\cdot}6\ \text{s}^{-1}$, so that $\tau_S = 2{\cdot}73 \times 10^{-2}$ s.

We may now derive values of ΔA_F, the optical density displacement resulting from the faster relaxation, by subtracting values of ΔA_S read off the back-extrapolated line in the plot at the corresponding t.

$10^3 t$ (s)	1	2	3	4	5	10
$\ln \Delta A_S$	1·345	1·308	1·270	1·235	1·200	1·017
ΔA_S	3·84	3·70	3·56	3·44	3·32	2·76
ΔA_F	2·03	1·47	1·07	0·76	0·55	0·12
$\ln \Delta A_F$	0·708	0·385	0·068	−0·274	−0·598	−2·12

Then a plot of $\ln \Delta A_F$ versus t should be linear with gradient $-\tau_F^{-1}$. This plot is linear with gradient of $-323\ \text{s}^{-1}$ so that $\tau_F = 3{\cdot}1 \times 10^{-3}$ s.

For the isolated relaxation, with characteristic relaxation time τ_S, associated with the equilibrium

$$\text{Hb} + \text{O}_2 \underset{k_b}{\overset{k_f}{\rightleftharpoons}} \text{HbO}_2$$

the relationship (derived in the textbooks) is

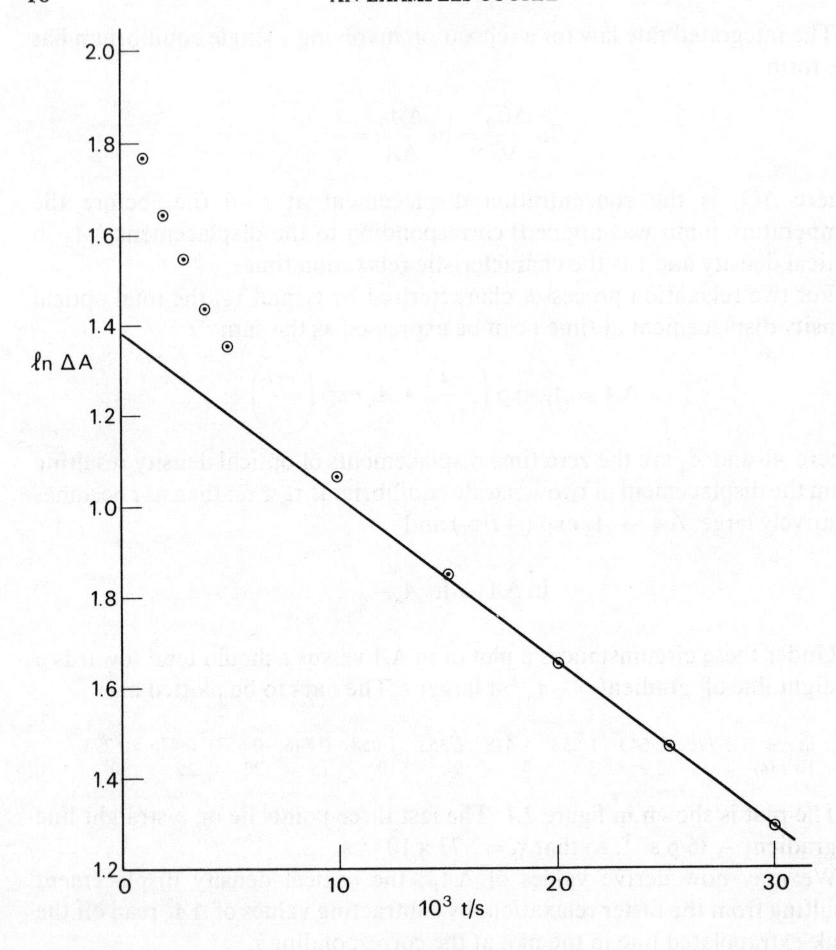

Figure 2.1

$$\tau_S^{-1} = k_b + k_f([\text{Hb}] + [O_2])$$

so that a linear plot of τ_S^{-1} versus $[\text{Hb}]+[O_2]$ should result. Combination of the result derived above with the three given values of τ_S yields the array:

τ_S (ms)	27·3	11·2	7·86	5·43
τ_S^{-1} (s^{-1})	36·6	89·3	127	184
$10^6([\text{Hb}]+[O_2])$ (mol dm^{-3})	5·3	25	39	60

The linear plot has intercept $k_b = 22\ s^{-1}$, while the gradient is $k_f = 2{\cdot}7 \times 10^6\ dm^3\ mol^{-1}\ s^{-1}$.

Note: The integrated rate law for a relaxation process involving a single equilibrium of the form $A + B \rightleftharpoons C$ is applicable for methods other than the temperature jump method, e.g. pressure jump, electric field jump, as concerned in problems 23 and 24. However when the perturbation is effected by a photolytic flash, it must be remembered that the equilibrium system will be relaxing back to its original equilibrium, not a new one: this situation will be encountered in exercise problems 51 and 58.

SECTION THREE

THE KINETIC ANALYSIS OF NON-CHAIN MECHANISMS

Example 9

Consecutive reactions, metastable intermediate, exact integrated rate law for consecutive first order reactions.

The thermal decomposition of phenyl-n-butyldiazirine (A) in dimethylsulphoxide solvent occurs by way of two consecutive unimolecular reactions. The first is isomerisation to 1-phenyl-1-diazopentane (B) and the second is decomposition of B to an organic product (C) and nitrogen gas, as follows:

$$\text{(N=N)C(Ph)(C}_4\text{H}_9\text{)}\ \text{(A)} \xrightarrow{k_1} \text{N}_2\text{=C(Ph)(C}_4\text{H}_9\text{)}\ \text{(B)} \xrightarrow{k_2} \text{C} + \text{N}_2$$

At 373·5 K, values of the rate constants have been established as $k_1 = 6{\cdot}8 \times 10^{-4}\ \text{s}^{-1}$ and $k_2 = 2{\cdot}2 \times 10^{-4}\ \text{s}^{-1}$. Starting with pure A at 373·5 K, how long should the reaction be allowed to proceed to generate a maximum concentration of B and what fraction of the initial concentration of A ($[\text{A}]_0$) would this be?

Confirm that the maximum fractional yield of B is given by the equation

$$\frac{[\text{B}]}{[\text{A}]_0} = \left(\frac{k_2}{k_1}\right)^{(k_2/(k_1 - k_2))}$$

and show that this is a general result for two consecutive unimolecular steps.
Source: Lin, M. T. H. and Jennings, B. M. (1977) *Canadian Journal of Chemistry*, **55**, p. 3596. (Canada)

Solution

For the mechanism composed of two consecutive unimolecular steps

$$A \xrightarrow{k_1} B \xrightarrow{k_2} \text{products}$$

the differential rate law for the rate of formation of B will be

$$\frac{d[B]}{dt} = k_1[A] - k_2[B]$$

$$= k_1[A]_0 \exp(-k_1 t) - k_2[B]$$

taking account of the integrated rate law for the removal of A

$$\ln\left(\frac{[A]}{[A]_0}\right) = -k_1 t$$

The integrated form of this equation is

$$[B] = [A]_0 \frac{k_1}{k_1 - k_2}\{\exp(-k_2 t) - \exp(-k_1 t)\} \qquad (\text{for } k_1 > k_2)$$

For a maximum in [B] (in the absence of any possibility of a minimum)

$$\frac{d[B]}{dt} = [A]_0 \frac{k_1}{k_1 - k_2}\{k_2 \exp(-k_2 t) - k_1 \exp(-k_1 t)\} = 0$$

Hence we must have the equation

$$k_2 \exp(-k_2 t) - k_1 \exp(-k_1 t) = 0$$

and upon taking logarithms we derive

$$\ln k_2 - k_2 t = \ln k_1 - k_1 t$$

so that upon rearrangement we obtain the solution

$$t = \frac{\ln\left(\dfrac{k_1}{k_2}\right)}{k_1 - k_2} \qquad \text{(i)}$$

and upon inserting the rate constant values given we obtain

$$t = \frac{\ln\left(\dfrac{6 \cdot 8}{2 \cdot 2}\right)}{4 \cdot 6 \times 10^{-4}} = 2 \cdot 45 \times 10^3 \text{ s} = 40 \cdot 9 \text{ min.}$$

Now at this time we will have

$$\frac{[B]}{[A]_0} = \frac{k_1}{k_1 - k_2}\{\exp(-k_2 t) - \exp(-k_1 t)\} \qquad \text{(ii)}$$

$$= \frac{6{\cdot}8}{4{\cdot}6}\{\exp(-2{\cdot}2 \times 0{\cdot}245) - \exp(-6{\cdot}8 \times 0{\cdot}245)\}$$

$$= 0{\cdot}58$$

According to the equation given we should also have

$$\frac{[B]}{[A]_0} = \left(\frac{k_2}{k_1}\right)^{(k_2/(k_1-k_2))}$$

$$= \left(\frac{2{\cdot}2}{6{\cdot}8}\right)^{(2{\cdot}2/4{\cdot}6)}$$

$$= 0{\cdot}58$$

Thus this calculated value is in agreement with the previous one.
In order to derive this result, we return to equation (i) to derive

$$k_1 t = \frac{k_1}{k_1 - k_2} \ln\left(\frac{k_1}{k_2}\right)$$

so that

$$\exp(-k_1 t) = \left(\frac{k_2}{k_1}\right)^{k_1/(k_1-k_2)}$$

Similarly we would derive

$$\exp(-k_2 t) = \left(\frac{k_2}{k_1}\right)^{k_2/(k_1-k_2)}$$

Upon substitution for the exponential terms in equation (ii) we obtain

$$\frac{[B]}{[A]_0} = \frac{k_1}{k_1 - k_2}\left\{\left(\frac{k_2}{k_1}\right)^{k_2/(k_1-k_2)} - \left(\frac{k_2}{k_1}\right)^{k_1/(k_1-k_2)}\right\}$$

$$= \frac{k_1}{k_1 - k_2}\left(\frac{k_2}{k_1}\right)^{k_2/(k_1-k_2)}\left(1 - \frac{k_2}{k_1}\right)$$

$$= \left(\frac{k_2}{k_1}\right)^{k_2/(k_1-k_2)}$$

which is therefore a general result for all pairs of consecutive unimolecular reactions.
(From the complexity of the above analysis, it can be appreciated that more complex mechanisms are not amenable to this approach.)

Example 10

Steady (stationary) state approximation, steady state analysis of rate law, consecutive reactions, mass spectrometry.

The thermal decomposition of hydrogen peroxide (H_2O_2) vapour in a suitably-aged reaction vessel is a homogeneous gas phase reaction, first order in $[H_2O_2]$. At 754 K, with initial concentration $[H_2O_2]_0 = 3{\cdot}2 \times 10^{-5}$ mol dm^{-3} in the presence of water vapour with $[H_2O] = 6{\cdot}4 \times 10^{-4}$ mol dm^{-3}, the initial step is

$$H_2O_2 + H_2O \rightarrow 2OH\cdot + H_2O \quad (1)$$

followed by

$$OH\cdot + H_2O_2 \rightarrow HO_2\cdot + H_2O \quad (2)$$

(Dots denote free radical species).

Two possible subsequent reaction steps are

$$OH\cdot + HO_2\cdot \rightarrow H_2O + O_2 \quad (3)$$

and

$$HO_2\cdot + HO_2\cdot \rightarrow H_2O_2 + O_2 \quad (4)$$

(*a*) Show that mechanism A (steps 1, 2 and 3) and mechanism B (steps 1, 2 and 4) both predict identical rate laws.

(*b*) Established values of the rate constants (from other work) under these conditions are $k_1 = 42{\cdot}9$ dm^3 mol^{-1} s^{-1}, $k_2 = 3 \times 10^9$ dm^3 mol^{-1} s^{-1}, $k_3 = 2 \times 10^{10}$ dm^3 mol^{-1} s^{-1} and $k_4 = 5 \times 10^9$ dm^3 mol^{-1} s^{-1}. Mass spectrometric sampling of the reacting system in the early stages of reaction showed that the steady state concentration of HO_2 radicals was below the detection limit of 6×10^{-7} mol dm^{-3}. Which mechanism may be eliminated as a possibility?

Source: Tessier, A. and Forst, W. (1974) *Canadian Journal of Chemistry*, **52**, p. 794. (Canada)

Solution

(*a*) We may apply the steady state approximation to the reactive radical species OH and HO_2. If we use R_x to denote the rate of reaction x, for mechanism A we shall have the equations

$$\frac{d[OH]}{dt} = 2R_1 - R_2 - R_3 = 0 \quad \text{(i)}$$

$$\frac{d[HO_2]}{dt} = R_2 - R_3 = 0 \quad \text{(ii)}$$

The overall rate of decomposition of H_2O_2 for mechanism A is given as

$$-\frac{d[H_2O_2]}{dt} = R_1 + R_2 \tag{iii}$$

Equation (i) combined with equation (ii) yields

$$2R_1 - 2R_2 = 0$$

and substitution into equation (iii) yields

$$-\frac{d[H_2O_2]}{dt} = 2R_1 = 2k_1[H_2O_2][H_2O]$$

with the last equality produced by applying the Law of Mass Action to the elementary reaction equation (1). This predicts overall first order kinetics since $[H_2O] \gg [H_2O_2]$ and the production of H_2O in steps (2) and (3) will have an insignificant effect on the total water vapour concentration.

For mechanism B, the application of the steady state approximation yields the equations

$$\frac{d[OH]}{dt} = 2R_1 - R_2 = 0 \tag{iv}$$

$$\frac{d[HO_2]}{dt} = R_2 - 2R_4 = 0 \tag{v}$$

while the overall rate of decomposition is expressed as

$$-\frac{d[H_2O_2]}{dt} = R_1 + R_2 - R_4 \tag{vi}$$

On substitution of (iv) and (v) into (vi) we obtain

$$-\frac{d[H_2O_2]}{dt} = 2R_1 = 2k_1[H_2O_2][H_2O]$$

Thus the two mechanisms lead to identical rate laws.

(*b*) On the basis of mechanism A and equation (ii) we have on applying the Law of Mass Action to the elementary steps

$$k_2[OH][H_2O_2] = k_3[HO_2][OH]$$

i.e.
$$[HO_2] = \frac{k_2[H_2O_2]}{k_3}$$

In the early stages we can assume insignificant decomposition of H_2O_2 so that with insertion of the initial concentration and the given rate constant values

$$[HO_2] = \frac{3\times 10^9 \times 3{\cdot}2\times 10^{-5}}{2\times 10^{10}} = 4{\cdot}8\times 10^{-6}\ \text{mol dm}^{-3}.$$

This is evidently well in excess of the minimum $[HO_2]$ which could have been detected, so that mechanism A is eliminated as a possibility.

On the basis of mechanism B and equations (iv) and (v) we have

$$R_1 = R_4$$

i.e.

$$k_1[H_2O_2][H_2O] = k_4[HO_2]^2$$

Using the rate constant values given and the initial concentration of H_2O_2

$$[HO_2] = \left(\frac{k_1[H_2O_2][H_2O]}{k_4}\right)^{1/2}$$

$$= \left(\frac{42{\cdot}9\times 3{\cdot}2\times 10^{-5}\times 6{\cdot}4\times 10^{-4}}{5\times 10^9}\right)^{1/2}$$

$$= 1{\cdot}3\times 10^{-8}\ \text{mol dm}^{-3}$$

Thus mechanism B leads to a predicted steady state concentration of HO_2 which is well below the minimum which could have been detected (6×10^{-7} mol dm^{-3}), so that this mechanism is possible.

Example 11

Steady (stationary) state approximation, steady state concentration measurement, consecutive reactions—integrated rate law, pseudo-zero order reaction, induction period, homogeneous catalysis.

The reaction in aqueous solution between I_3^- and $S_2O_3^{2-}$ ions has been studied by rapidly mixing solutions of $K_2S_2O_8$, KI and $Na_2S_2O_3$, when I_2 was generated by the slow reaction (first order in both reactants)

$$S_2O_8^{2-} + 2I^- \rightarrow 2SO_4^{2-} + I_2 \qquad (1)$$

with a known rate constant $k_1 = 3{\cdot}00\times 10^{-3}$ dm^3 mol^{-1} s^{-1} at 298 K. I_3^- is then rapidly formed in the maintenance of the equilibrium

$$I^- + I_2 \rightleftharpoons I_3^-$$

A bright platinum foil electrode dipped into the solution measured the reversible potential (E) due to the I_3^-/I^- redox system and this was calibrated for the reaction solutions according to the equation

$$E\,(\text{mV}) = 420{\cdot}9 + 12{\cdot}53\ \ln\,[I_3^-]$$

The following results were obtained for a solution at 298 K with initial concentrations of $[K_2S_2O_8]=0{\cdot}020$ mol dm^{-3}, $[KI]=0{\cdot}040$ mol dm^{-3} and $[Na_2S_2O_3]=2{\cdot}00\times10^{-3}$ mol dm^{-3} as a function of time (t):

E (mV)	187·0	189·0	190·5	191·7	193·0
t (s)	0	60	100	130	160

(*a*) Show that these results are in accordance with a fast reaction, first order in each of I_3^- and $S_2O_3^{2-}$, when the reaction stoichiometric equation is

$$2S_2O_3^{2-}+I_3^- \rightarrow S_4O_6^{2-}+3I^- \qquad (2)$$

and evaluate the effective second order rate constant, k_2.

(*b*) Assuming that mixing can be made extremely rapidly and that the I^-/I_3^- equilibrium is established effectively instantaneously, calculate the time required for I_3^- to achieve 99% of its steady state concentration.

Source: Rao, T. S. and Mali, S. I. (1974) *Zeitschrift fur Naturforschung*, **29A**, p. 141. (India)

Solution

(*a*) The first point to realise is that $[S_2O_8^{2-}]$ and $[I^-]$ are very much larger than $[S_2O_3^{2-}]$, so that only the last concentration will change significantly during the early stages of the reaction. Also I_3^- will be a steady state, reactive intermediate if reaction (2) is much faster than reaction (1). The reactions can be represented effectively by the equations

$$S_2O_8^{2-}+3I^- \rightarrow 2SO_4^{2-}+I_3^-$$
$$I_3^-+2S_2O_3^{2-} \rightarrow S_4O_6^{2-}+3I^-$$

taking account of the rapid equilibration of I^- and I_3^- and making clear the homogeneous catalytic role of I^-. If both reactions are first order in both reactants with effective second order rate constants k_1 and k_2 respectively, the steady state condition becomes

$$k_1[I^-][S_2O_8^{2-}]=k_2[I_3^-][S_2O_3^{2-}]$$

Only if k_2 turns out to be a constant for the data given will the second reaction be proven to be first order in each reactant. Since the left hand side, involving large concentrations, will be expected to be constant (i.e. reaction (1) can be regarded as pseudo-zero order) in the early stages of removal of $S_2O_3^{2-}$, our task becomes that of proving that the product $[I_3^-][S_2O_3^{2-}]$ is constant at each value of t. We postulate that I_3^- (I_2) is produced at a constant rate (R_I) with the numerical value

$$\begin{aligned}R_I &= k_1[I^-][S_2O_8^{2-}]\\ &= 3{\cdot}00\times10^{-3}\times4{\cdot}0\times10^{-2}\times2{\cdot}0\times10^{-2}\\ &= 2{\cdot}4\times10^{-6}\ \text{mol dm}^{-3}\ \text{s}^{-1}\end{aligned}$$

Thus at time t after the start of reaction, the total concentration of I_3^- which has been generated and gone on to react in the fast subsequent reaction (2) is $2{\cdot}4 \times 10^{-6}t$ mol dm^{-3} and this will be equal to half of the concentration of $S_2O_3^{2-}$ removed at time t. Thus we can calculate $[S_2O_3^{2-}]$ remaining at time t and also, from the measured E and its calibration, we can evaluate the steady state concentration of I_3^-. The sequence of the calculation is tabulated below:

t (s)	0	60	100	130	160
$10^3 R_I t$ (mol dm^{-3})	0	0·144	0·240	0·312	0·384
$10^3[S_2O_3^{2-}]$ (mol dm^{-3})	2·00	1·712	1·520	1·376	1·232
E (mV)	187·0	189·0	190·5	191·7	193·0
$10^8[I_3^-]$ (mol dm^{-3})	0·782	0·917	1·033	1·137	1·262
$10^{11}[I_3^-][S_2O_3^{2-}]$ (mol^2 dm^{-6})	1·56	1·57	1·57	1·56	1·55

Since the variations in the last row are insignificant, it proves the second order rate law applied to reaction (2), while the small concentrations of I_3^- show that it is correct to regard this species as a steady state intermediate subject to removal in a fast reaction. (Note that the usage of the terms *fast* and *slow* is referred to the rate when all species have unit concentrations: under the steady state conditions involved in this problem, the actual rates of reactions (1) and (2) are equal).

The value of k_2 can be calculated using the average value of the bottom row of the above table (i.e. $1{\cdot}56 \times 10^{-11}$ mol^2 dm^{-6}). Hence we have

$$k_2 = \frac{R_I}{[I_3^-][S_2O_3^{2-}]}$$

$$= \frac{2{\cdot}4 \times 10^{-6}}{1{\cdot}56 \times 10^{-11}}$$

$$= 1{\cdot}5 \times 10^5 \text{ dm}^3 \text{ mol}^{-1} \text{ s}^{-1}$$

(*b*) Here we are concerned with the induction time of the steady state, i.e. the period at the start of the reaction when it is not correct to take $d[I_3^-]/dt = 0$ since $[I_3^-]$ rises at a finite rate towards its steady state value. Since the steady state concentrations calculated above are so small, we can regard the time involved here as being short enough for $[S_2O_3^{2-}]$ to be considered as unaltered from its initial value. Thus $k_2[S_2O_3^{2-}]$ can be equated to a pseudo-first order rate constant, ${}_1k_2$. In differential form the rate law can be written

$$\frac{d[I_3^-]}{dt} = R_I - {}_1k_2[I_3^-]$$

Collecting the variables and integrating we shall have

$$\int_0^{I_3^-} \frac{d[I_3^-]}{R_I - {}_1k_2[I_3^-]} = ({}_1k_2)^{-1} \ln\left(\frac{R_I}{R_I - {}_1k_2[I_3^-]}\right)$$

$$= \int_0^t dt = t$$

The steady state concentration of I_3^- is defined as

$$[I_3^-]_{ss} = \frac{R_I}{k_2[S_2O_3^{2-}]}$$

$$= \frac{2{\cdot}4 \times 10^{-6}}{1{\cdot}5 \times 10^5 \times 2{\cdot}0 \times 10^{-3}}$$

$$= 8{\cdot}0 \times 10^{-9} \text{ mol dm}^{-3}$$

and 99% of this is $7{\cdot}9 \times 10^{-9}$ mol dm^{-3}, which is then put into the above integrated equation to yield

$$t = (300)^{-1} \ln\left(\frac{2{\cdot}4 \times 10^{-6}}{2{\cdot}4 \times 10^{-6} - 300 \times 7{\cdot}9 \times 10^{-9}}\right)$$

$$= 1{\cdot}5 \times 10^{-2} \text{ s}$$

where $\quad {}_1k_2 = k_2[S_2O_3^{2-}] = 1{\cdot}5 \times 10^5 \times 2{\cdot}0 \times 10^{-3} = 300 \text{ s}^{-1}$

In this time $R_I t = 2{\cdot}4 \times 10^{-6} \times 1{\cdot}5 \times 10^{-2} = 3{\cdot}6 \times 10^{-8}$ mol dm^{-3}, which justifies our assumption that $[S_2O_3^{2-}]$ is unchanged effectively from its initial value. Hence after this very short time we would be justified in applying the steady state approximation to I_3^-, provided that mixing was rapid enough.

Example 12

Pre-equilibrium, rate-determining step, initial rates, pseudo-first order reaction.

In chlorine water a rapid equilibrium is established, represented as

$$Cl_2(+H_2O) \rightleftharpoons H^+ + Cl^- + HOCl$$

between dissolved Cl_2 and hypochlorous acid (HOCl), for which the equilibrium constant at 298 K is $5{\cdot}0 \times 10^{-4}$ mol^2 dm^{-6}, applicable for the conditions below.

When the total initial concentration of dissolved chlorine in water was $1{\cdot}5 \times 10^{-3}$ mol dm^{-3} and the initial concentration of dissolved propan-2-ol was $2{\cdot}01 \times 10^{-2}$ mol dm^{-3}, the latter was oxidised according to the initial rate law

$$-\frac{d[\text{oxidant}]}{dt} = k_{obs}[\text{oxidant}]$$

oxidant refers to the combination of Cl_2 and HOCl. At pH = 1 and 298 K, it was found that addition of chloride ions ($>5 \times 10^{-3}$ mol dm^{-3}) to the solution accelerated the rate, and a plot of $(k_{obs})^{-1}$ versus $[Cl^-]^{-1}$ was linear with intercept (at $[Cl^-]=0$) of $69{\cdot}0$ s and gradient of $3{\cdot}4 \times 10^{-1}$ mol dm^{-3} s.

Use these data to identify which of the particular species in solution, Cl_2 or HOCl, acts as the coreactant with the alcohol in the rate-determining step, and evaluate its rate constant under these conditions.

Source: Venkatasubramanian, N. and Srinivasan, N. S. (1972) *Indian Journal of Chemistry*, **10**, p. 1085. (India)

Solution

The two possibilities for the rate-determining step can be written

$$Cl_2(aq) + \text{propan-2-ol} \rightarrow \text{products} \quad (1)$$

$$HOCl(aq) + \text{propan-2-ol} \rightarrow \text{products} \quad (2)$$

with rate constants k_1 and k_2 respectively.

The initial equilibrium is rapid and so will be maintained throughout the reaction as a pre-equilibrium written as

$$Cl_2(+H_2O) \rightleftharpoons H^+ + Cl^- + HOCl$$

and we may designate the equilibrium constant as

$$K = \frac{[H^+][Cl^-][HOCl]}{[Cl_2]}$$
$$= 5{\cdot}0 \times 10^{-4}\ \text{mol}^2\ \text{dm}^{-6}$$

Now the addition of Cl^- ions as such will push the pre-equilibrium over to the left-hand side and thus increase $[Cl_2]$ at the expense of [HOCl]. Since we are told that this results in an increased rate of oxidation, this strongly indicates that reaction (1) is the rate-determining step, but we must prove that this leads to a prediction of the observed linear plot of $(k_{obs})^{-1}$ versus $[Cl^-]^{-1}$ under the pseudo-first order conditions represented by [oxidant]= $[HOCl]+[Cl_2]=1{\cdot}5\times10^{-3}$ mol dm^{-3} and [alcohol]$=2{\cdot}01\times10^{-2}$ mol dm^{-3}. By rearrangement of the equilibrium constant expression we derive the fraction of total chlorine present as Cl_2

$$\frac{[Cl_2]}{[\text{oxidant}]} = 1 + \frac{K}{[H^+][Cl^-]}$$

If (1) is considered as the rate-determining step then the overall rate is

$$-\frac{d[\text{oxidant}]}{dt} = k_1[Cl_2][\text{alcohol}] = k_{obs}[\text{oxidant}]$$

and

$$k_{obs} = k_1[\text{alcohol}]\frac{[Cl_2]}{[\text{oxidant}]} = 1 + \frac{\dfrac{k_1[\text{alcohol}]}{K}}{[H^+][Cl^-]}$$

Upon inversion of both sides we obtain the equation

$$k_{obs}^{-1} = (k_1[\text{alcohol}])^{-1} + \frac{K}{k_1[\text{alcohol}][H^+]}[Cl^-]^{-1}$$

Thus at constant pH (i.e. $[H^+]$) this predicts the required linear plot of $(k_{obs})^{-1}$ versus $[Cl^-]^{-1}$, where the intercept is the reciprocal of k_1[alcohol] and the ratio of the gradient to the intercept is $K/[H^+]$. The values of these parameters given must lead to the given value of K. The data given yield a gradient to intercept ratio of $3{\cdot}4 \times 10^{-1}/69{\cdot}0 = 4{\cdot}93 \times 10^{-3}$ mol dm^{-3} which leads to $K = 4{\cdot}93 \times 10^{-4}$ mol^2 dm^{-6} since pH$=1$ corresponds to $[H^+] =$ 0·1 mol dm^{-3}, and this is in acceptable agreement with the given value of $5{\cdot}0 \times 10^{-4}$ mol^2 dm^{-6}. Also the intercept of 69·0 s is the reciprocal of $k_1[\text{alcohol}] = k_1\ 2{\cdot}01 \times 10^{-2}$, from which we derive $k_1 = 0{\cdot}721$ dm^3 mol^{-1} s^{-1}.

It can be shown by similar analysis that, had step (2) involving HOCl as the coreactant with the alcohol been the effective rate determining step of oxidation, then a linear plot of $(k_{obs})^{-1}$ versus $[Cl^-]$ should have been produced.

Also since $K = 5{\cdot}0 \times 10^{-4}$ mol dm^{-3} then by rearrangement of the expression for the equilibrium constant we obtain

$$\frac{[Cl_2]}{[HOCl]} = \frac{[H^+][Cl^-]}{K}$$

$$= 200[Cl^-] \text{ for } [H^+] = 0{\cdot}1 \text{ mol dm}^{-3}$$

Hence Cl_2 is the predominant component of the total oxidant concentration when $[Cl^-] > 5 \times 10^{-3}$ mol dm^{-3}, the condition concerned in this problem.

Example 13

Radioactive isotope, kinetic isotope effects (insignificant), mechanism and isotopic labelling, elementary reaction (criteria), specific radioactivity.

The reaction of dithionite ($S_2O_4^{2-}$) ions with disulphide (S_2^{2-}) ions in 4·0 mol dm^{-3} NaOH aqueous solution proceeds by the mechanism

$$S_2O_4^{2-} + 2OH^- \rightarrow SO_2^{2-} + SO_3^{2-} + H_2O \qquad (1)$$

$$SO_2^{2-} + S_2^{2-} \rightarrow S_2O_2^{2-} + S^{2-} \qquad (2)$$

$$S_2O_2^{2-} + OH^- \rightarrow S^{2-} + HSO_3^- \qquad (3)$$

$$HSO_3^- + OH^- \rightarrow SO_3^{2-} + H_2O \qquad (4)$$

Starting with S_2^{2-} ions containing radioactive ^{35}S and with $S_2O_4^{2-}$ ions containing no radioactive isotope, show that the relative values of the specific radioactivities of the products S^{2-} and SO_3^{2-} allow differentiation between the possible structures of the intermediate $S_2O_2^{2-}$ ion

$$OSSO^{2-} \text{ (symmetric) (I)} \quad \text{or} \quad SSO_2^{2-} \text{ (asymmetric) (II)}$$

on the basis that exchange of sulphur between the ionic species does not occur. Discuss the likelihood of reactions (2) and (3) being of an elementary nature in the two cases.

The relative specific radioactivities in one experiment were measured as follows:

Starting materials: $Na_2S_2O_4 = 0$, $Na_2S_2 = 1{\cdot}0$
Products: $S^{2-} = 0{\cdot}95$, $SO_3^{2-} = 0{\cdot}007$

Which structure of $S_2O_2^{2-}$ accords most closely with these results?

Source: Aten, A. H. W. (1975) *Radiochimica Acta*, **22**, p. 93. (Netherlands)

Solution

Writing the detailed mechanism for reaction of $^{35}S_2^{2-}$ we shall have

$$S_2O_4^{2-} + 2OH^- \rightarrow OSO^{2-} + SO_3^{2-} + H_2O \qquad (1)$$

$$OSO^{2-} + {}^{35}S_2^{2-} \rightarrow O^{35}SSO^{2-}\text{(I) or } {}^{35}SSO_2^{2-}\text{(II)} + {}^{35}S^{2-} \qquad (2)$$

It would evidently be thoroughly unrealistic in terms of the number of bonds required to be broken and formed to regard reaction (2) proceeding as

$$OSO^{2-} + {}^{35}S_2^{2-} \rightarrow ({}^{35}SO)_2^{2-} + S^{2-}$$

Accepting that ^{35}S and the normal isotope ^{32}S are chemically indistinguishable (i.e. no isotopic differentiation), we see that the two sulphur atoms are equivalent in structure I but not in structure II. At the same time we recognise that kinetic isotope effects will be insignificant, since it is usually only in the case of the lightest elements (particularly H and D) that isotope effects achieve any significance.

Step (3) would then proceed as follows for the two structures of $S_2O_2^{2-}$:

Structure I

$$O^{35}SSO^{2-} + OH^- \rightarrow H^{35}SO_3^- + S^{2-} \qquad (3a)$$

$$\rightarrow HSO_3^- + {}^{35}S^{2-} \qquad (3b)$$

with both pathways equally likely because of the chemical equivalence of the two sulphur atoms. Hence it can be seen that the combination of step (2) with step (3*a*) produces an equal distribution of ^{35}S between SO_3^{2-} and S^{2-} on taking account of step (4) which can involve no sulphur isotope exchange

$$HSO_3^- + OH^- \rightarrow SO_3^{2-} + H_2O \qquad (4)$$

However step (2) combined with step (3*b*) produces all of the ^{35}S in the form of $^{35}S^{2-}$ with none in the form of SO_3^{2-}. Hence the overall result of steps (2) and (3) in the case of structure I is to lead to specific radioactivities of S^{2-} and SO_3^{2-} products in the ratio of 0·75 to 0·25 respectively. The same result is produced if the ion in reaction (2) is considered to be $^{35}SS^{2-}$.

Structure II

$$^{35}SSO_2^{2-} + OH^- \rightarrow HSO_3^- + {}^{35}S^{2-}$$

There is little possibility here that HSO_3^- and hence the SO_3^{2-} produced in the subsequent step (4) could contain ^{35}S, since that would entail a considerable breaking and formation of bonds which is unlikely to occur. Thus in the case of structure II we should expect only the S^{2-} product to show radioactivity with the same specific activity as the starting S_2^{2-}.

From what has been said above, it is clear that structure II need only involve elementary reactions such as steps (2) and (3), with only one bond being broken and one new bond being formed in each act at the molecular level. However the involvement of structure I would require considerable rearrangements of atoms in each of steps (2) and (3), which are unlikely to be consistent with elementary processes. On this basis alone, we should favour structure II as the likely intermediate. This is confirmed by the measured relative specific activities, where those of 0·95 and 0·007 for S^{2-} and SO_3^{2-} are much closer to the 1 and 0 expected for II than to the 0·75 and 0·25 expected for I.

SECTION FOUR

THE KINETIC ANALYSIS OF CHAIN REACTION MECHANISMS

Example 14

Straight chain reaction (liquid phase), steady state approximation, kinetic chain length, inhibition, initial rates method, Henry's law (thermodynamic), gas burette.

In the presence of excess HCl, stannous (Sn(II)) ions are oxidised to Sn(IV) by molecular oxygen dissolved in the aqueous solution. The table below gives the initial rates (R_i) of absorption of O_2 by a volume of 0·010 dm^3 of a well-stirred solution of $SnCl_2$ of initial concentration (C) in 2 M HCl as a function of the partial pressure of O_2 (P) in nitrogen at total pressure of 101·3 kPa at 293 K, obtained using an automatic gas burette:

Experiment number	1	2	3	4	5	6
$10^5 R_i$ (mol min^{-1})	2·1	1·0	0·55	0·21	1·5	0·94
10^{-5}P (Pa)	9·70	5·92	3·98	2·07	9·70	9·70
C (mol dm^{-3})	0·050	0·050	0·050	0·050	0·025	0·010

(*a*) Show that these data are consistent with chain mechanism

$$Sn(II)+O_2 \xrightarrow{H^+} Sn(III)+HO_2 \quad (1)$$

$$Sn(III)+O_2 \xrightarrow{H^+} Sn(IV)+HO_2 \quad (2)$$

$$HO_2+Sn(II) \xrightarrow{H^+} Sn(III)+H_2O_2 \quad (3)$$

$$H_2O_2+Sn(II) \xrightarrow{H^+} Sn(IV)+2H_2O \quad (4)$$

$$Sn(III)+Sn(III) \longrightarrow Sn(II)+Sn(IV) \quad (5)$$

on the assumption that the chains are long.

(*b*) On addition of sufficient benzoquinone base (known to act by removing Sn(III)), the initial rate is depressed to a limiting value. Predict the order of the reaction under the limiting condition. The limiting initial rate for $P = 9{\cdot}70 \times 10^5$ Pa and $C = 0{\cdot}050$ mol dm^{-3} is $R_i = 1{\cdot}9 \times 10^{-6}$ mol min^{-1}; calculate the kinetic chain length for these conditions which would apply in the absence of the base. (The Henry's law constant applicable to these O_2 solutions is $9{\cdot}70 \times 10^8$ Pa dm^3 mol^{-1}.)

Source: Kutner, E. A. and Matseevskii, B. P. (1969) *Kinetics and Catalysis* (English translation of *Kinetika i Kataliz*), **10**, p. 812. (U.S.S.R.)

Solution

We may first analyse the kinetic behaviour predicted by the given chain mechanism, which requires the identification of the nature of each step. Step (1) represents initiation, producing the chain carrier Sn(III), so that step (5) represents termination in removing this chain carrier. Sn(III) is a reactant in step (2) and is regenerated as a product in step (3), so that together these are the propagation steps. Step (4) is presumed to be a rapid consecutive reaction to (3) and exerts no influence on the rate of consumption of O_2; hence it can be ignored.

The obvious course of kinetic analysis is to apply the steady state approximation. This is a linear chain reaction (steps (2) and (3) each involve only one Sn(III) ion), so that the steady state approximation may be applied through the statement that the rate of initiation must equal the rate of termination (i.e. the concentration of the chain carrier, Sn(III), is at steady state). Thus we shall have the equation

$$k_1[\mathrm{Sn(II)}][\mathrm{O_2}] = 2k_5[\mathrm{Sn(III)}]^2$$

with the coefficient 2 inserted to take account of the two Sn(III) ions removed in reaction (5). Rearrangement of this equation yields

$$[\mathrm{Sn(III)}] = \left(\frac{k_1}{2k_5}\right)^{1/2} [\mathrm{Sn(II)}]^{1/2}[\mathrm{O_2}]^{1/2} \qquad \text{(i)}$$

The full expression for the rate of consumption of O_2 will be

$$R_i = -\frac{d[\mathrm{O_2}]}{dt}$$
$$= k_1[\mathrm{Sn(II)}][\mathrm{O_2}] + k_2[\mathrm{Sn(III)}][\mathrm{O_2}]$$

and upon substituting for the steady state concentration of Sn(III) from (i)

$$R_i = k_1[\mathrm{Sn(II)}][\mathrm{O_2}] + k_2\left(\frac{k_1}{2k_5}\right)^{1/2} [\mathrm{Sn(II)}]^{1/2}[\mathrm{O_2}]^{3/2} \qquad \text{(ii)}$$

However we are told to assume that the chains are very long (i.e. the propagation rate is very much faster than the initiation rate) so that the first term on the right hand side of equation (ii) can be ignored. The predicted partial orders of the mechanism are thus $\frac{1}{2}$ in Sn(II) and $\frac{3}{2}$ in O_2.

(*a*) We may now set out to extract partial orders from the initial rate data by attempting to fit the equation of the form

$$R_i = k_n[\mathrm{Sn(II)}]^p[O_2]^q$$

i.e.
$$\ln R_i = \text{constant} + p \ln [\mathrm{Sn(II)}] + q \ln \mathrm{P}$$

We use P on the basis that the concentration of dissolved O_2 will be related to P through the Henry's law form $\mathrm{P} = K_H[O_2]$, where K_H is the Henry's law constant. Experiments 1, 2, 3 and 4 have [Sn(II)] constant, so that a plot of $\ln R_i$ versus ln P will have gradient q. Also experiments 1, 5 and 6 have P constant, so that a plot of $\ln R_i$ versus $\ln C$ should be linear with gradient p. The data for the plots are as follows:

Experiment number	1	2	3	4	5	6
$\ln (10^6 R_i)$	3·045	2·302	1·705	0·742	2·708	2·241
$\ln (10^{-5}\mathrm{P})$	2·272	1·778	1·381	0·728	—	—
$\ln (10^2 C)$	1·609	—	—	—	0·916	0·000

The plots are linear and yield $p = \frac{1}{2}$ and $q = \frac{3}{2}$ respectively, which are thus in agreement with the predictions from the mechanism.

(*b*) Since the benzoquinone base removes the chain carrier, its action represents inhibition of the chain reaction and in the limit the overall rate will have been depressed to that of the initiation step (1). Thus the predicted rate law for the fully-inhibited reaction will be

$$R_i^0 = k_1[\mathrm{Sn(II)}][O_2]$$

and the reaction will follow first order kinetics in each reactant and second order kinetics overall. The data given are the inhibited rate $R_i^0 = 1{\cdot}9 \times 10^{-6}$ mol min^{-1}, directly comparable with the uninhibited rate $R_i = 2{\cdot}1 \times 10^{-5}$ mol min^{-1} for the same reactant concentrations in experiment 1.

The kinetic chain length (L) is defined as the ratio of the propagation rate $(R_i - R_i^0)$ to the initiation rate (R_i^0) so that we derive

$$L = 1{\cdot}9 \times 10^{-5}/1{\cdot}9 \times 10^{-6} = 10$$

and since $R_i/R_i^0 = 11$, the assumption that the chains are long is justified.

Example 15

Straight chain reaction (gas phase), Arrhenius equation (composite Arrhenius parameters), steady state approximation, bond dissociation energy, heat of formation (thermodynamic).

The rate of the thermal decomposition of pure F_2O vapour at initial pressures in the range 1 to 100 kPa has been measured at temperatures in the range 501 to 583 K. The experimental rate law for the homogeneous reaction was established to be

$$-\frac{d[F_2O]}{dt} = k_I[F_2O]^2 + k_{II}[F_2O]^{3/2}$$

with

$$k_I = 7{\cdot}8 \times 10^{13} \exp(-19\,350\ \mathrm{K}/T)\ \mathrm{dm^3\ mol^{-1}\ s^{-1}}$$

and

$$k_{II} = 2{\cdot}3 \times 10^{10} \exp(-16\,910\ \mathrm{K}/T)\ \mathrm{dm^{3/2}\ mol^{-1/2}\ s^{-1}}.$$

Show that this rate law is consistent with the mechanism

$$F_2O + F_2O \rightarrow F + OF + F_2O \qquad (1)$$

$$F + F_2O \rightarrow F_2 + OF \qquad (2)$$

$$OF + OF \rightarrow O_2 + 2F \qquad (3)$$

$$2F + F_2O \rightarrow F_2 + F_2O \qquad (4)$$

Given $\Delta H_f(F_2O) = 24{\cdot}41$ kJ mol^{-1}, $D(F-F) = 160{\cdot}6$ kJ mol^{-1} and $D(O-O) = 498{\cdot}2$ kJ mol^{-1}, all at 540 K, and making a reasonable estimate for the Arrhenius activation energy of reaction (4) (see example 21), estimate the bond dissociation energies of the first and second $F-O$ bonds in F_2O and the Arrhenius activation energy of reaction (2).

Source: Czarnowski, J. and Schumacher, H. J. (1972) *Chemical Physics Letters*, **17**, p. 235. (Argentina)

Solution

As written, the mechanism of steps (1) to (4) constitutes a straight chain cycle. Step (1) represents initiation, being a unimolecular decomposition of a triatomic molecule, evidently in its second order, low pressure limiting region under these conditions (see example 20). In effect it furnishes two F atoms, since step (3) converts the OF radical product into an F atom. For a linear chain reaction proceeding under steady state conditions, the rates of initiation and termination must be equal (see preceding example), so that we can write the equation

$$2k_1[F_2O]^2 = 2k_4[F]^2[F_2O]$$

i.e.

$$[F] = \left(\frac{k_1[F_2O]}{k_4}\right)^{1/2} \tag{i}$$

The propagation steps (2) and (3) exert no effect on [F] since the sequence is simply F → OF → F.

The overall rate of disappearance of F_2O is given by the equation

$$-\frac{d[F_2O]}{dt} = k_1[F_2O]^2 + k_2[F][F_2O]$$

and upon substitution of equation (i) we obtain

$$-\frac{d[F_2O]}{dt} = k_1[F_2O]^2 + k_2\left(\frac{k_1}{k_4}\right)^{1/2}[F_2O]^{3/2}$$

This conforms with the experimental rate law with $k_{\text{I}} = k_1$ and $k_{\text{II}} = k_2(k_1/k_4)^{1/2}$. It follows that $k_1 = 7{\cdot}8 \times 10^{13} \exp(-19\,350\ \text{K}/T)$ dm³ mol⁻¹ s⁻¹ and upon identification with the Arrhenius equation form $k_1 = A_1 \exp(-E_1/RT)$, the Arrhenius activation energy of reaction (1) is indicated to be $E_1 = 19\,350 \times R = 160{\cdot}9$ kJ mol⁻¹. Since the activation energy of a unimolecular dissociation reaction is expected to be close to the dissociation energy of the bond being broken, we predict $D(\text{F}-\text{OF}) \approx 160{\cdot}9$ kJ mol⁻¹.

Since k_{II} is identified with $k_2(k_1/k_4)^{1/2}$ and each individual elementary reaction rate constant can be expressed in an Arrhenius equation form, then by taking logarithms and differentiating with respect to T, we obtain

$$\begin{aligned} E_{\text{II}} &= E_2 + \tfrac{1}{2}E_1 - \tfrac{1}{2}E_4 \\ &= 16\,910 \times R \\ &= 140{\cdot}6\ \text{kJ mol}^{-1} \end{aligned}$$

Since we have already estimated $E_1 = 160{\cdot}9$ kJ mol⁻¹, this leads to the equation

$$E_2 - \tfrac{1}{2}E_4 = 140{\cdot}6 - 80{\cdot}45 = 60{\cdot}15\ \text{kJ mol}^{-1}$$

Now E_4 represents the activation energy for a termolecular association of atoms and is therefore expected to be small and negative. In view of the relevant information presented in example 21, we could use $E_4 = -8$ kJ mol⁻¹ as a reasonable guess, which leads to an estimate of $E_2 \approx 56$ kJ mol⁻¹.

At the approximate median temperature of 540 K, where $D(\mathrm{F-OF})=160{\cdot}9\ \mathrm{kJ\ mol^{-1}}$, $\Delta H_f(\mathrm{F_2O})=24{\cdot}4\ \mathrm{kJ\ mol^{-1}}$, $D(\mathrm{F-F})=160{\cdot}6\ \mathrm{kJ\ mol^{-1}}$ and $D(\mathrm{O-O})=498{\cdot}2\ \mathrm{kJ\ mol^{-1}}$, we can construct a Hess Law cycle which will enable us to estimate $D(\mathrm{O-F})$. This is shown in figure 4.1. The numbers shown are enthalpy changes for the directions indicated by the arrows, in kJ per number of mols indicated. Since the total change around the cycle must

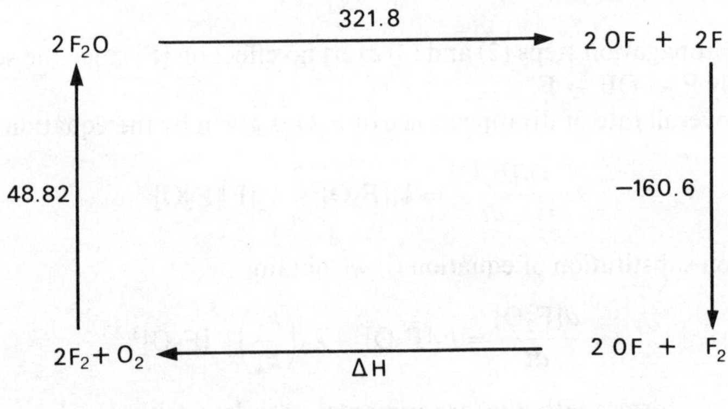

Figure 4.1

be zero, it follows that $\Delta H=160{\cdot}6-321{\cdot}8-48{\cdot}8=-210{\cdot}0$ kJ. By considering the rearrangement of bonds associated with ΔH, we obtain the equation

$$\Delta H = 2D(\mathrm{O-F}) - D(\mathrm{F-F}) - D(\mathrm{O-O})$$

where the only unknown is $D(\mathrm{O-F})$. Rearrangement and insertion of the values yields

$$D(\mathrm{O-F}) = \frac{-210{\cdot}0+160{\cdot}6+498{\cdot}2}{2} \simeq 224\ \mathrm{kJ\ mol^{-1}}$$

Example 16

Branched chain reaction, inhibition, explosion limits, diffusion coefficient, steady state approximation.

The explosion limits (boundaries) of stoichiometric mixtures of hydrogen and oxygen ($2H_2+O_2$) have been established in a closed reaction vessel, following the additions of either $C_2F_4Br_2$ (A) or CF_3Br (B).

(*a*) At a temperature of 898 K with additions of partial pressures (P_A) of A, the lowest (first) explosion limit was found at total pressures (P) as a function of P_A as follows:

P_A (Pa)	0	23·3	43·0
P (kPa)	0·553	0·608	0·660

(*b*) At a temperature of 733 K with additions of B at partial pressure P_B, the second explosion limit varied as follows:

P_B (Pa)	0	0·928	1·36	1·58
P (kPa)	2·541	2·320	2·189	2·115

On the basis that the only effective termination steps are the processes:

First limit only: $H \xrightarrow{\text{wall}} \frac{1}{2}H_2$ (diffusion-limited)

Second limit only: $H + O_2 + M \longrightarrow HO_2 + M$

Both limits: $\left.\begin{matrix} H + A \xrightarrow{k_A} \\ H + B \xrightarrow{k_B} \end{matrix}\right\}$ non-propagating products

where M represents any molecule in the system.

Use the above data to evaluate the rate constant ratios, k_A/k_1 at 898 K and k_B/k_1 at 733 K, where the rate constant k_1 applies to the reaction

$$H + O_2 \rightarrow OH + O \tag{1}$$

Source: Petrova, L. D., Azatyan, V. V., Baratov, A. N., Makeev, V. I. and Kondenko, E. E. (1976) *Izvestia Akademii Nauk S.S.S.R., Ser. Khim.*, p. 879 (in English translation). (U.S.S.R.)

Solution

The propagation mechanism of the H_2/O_2 reaction system is as follows:

$$H\cdot + O_2 \rightarrow OH\cdot + O\cdot \tag{1}$$

$$O\cdot + H_2 \rightarrow OH\cdot + H\cdot \tag{2}$$

$$OH\cdot + H_2 \rightarrow H_2O + H\cdot \tag{3}$$

(dots denote free radical species). This sums to a net reaction per cycle expressed by the overall equation

$$H\cdot + O_2 + 3H_2 \rightarrow 3H\cdot + 2H_2O$$

Thus the net rate of chain propagation (net 2H atoms generated per cycle) can be equated to $2k_1[H][O_2]$.

(*a*) At the first explosion limit in the absence of added gases, the propagation rate is balanced by the diffusion-limited heterogeneous destruction of hydrogen atoms at the walls. The rate of diffusion will be governed by the diffusion coefficient of hydrogen atoms in the stoichiometric mixture, which at a defined temperature will vary inversely with P. Hence we can express the diffusion coefficient as k_D^0/P, where k_D^0 is independent of P, and the rate of diffusion is $k_D^0[H]/P$, where [H] is the steady state concentration of hydrogen atoms in the bulk gas phase. In the presence of added A, the condition for the first explosion limit can therefore be expressed by equating the net propagation rate to the sum of the rates of the two effective termination processes

$$2k_1[\mathrm{H}][\mathrm{O_2}] = \frac{k_\mathrm{D}^0[\mathrm{H}]}{P} + k_\mathrm{A}[\mathrm{H}][\mathrm{A}] \qquad \text{(i)}$$

Equation (i) rearranges to the form

$$[\mathrm{O_2}] = \frac{k_\mathrm{D}^0}{2k_1 P} + \frac{k_\mathrm{A}[\mathrm{A}]}{2k_1}$$

i.e. with application of the ideal gas law

$$\mathrm{P_{O_2}} = \frac{RT\,k_\mathrm{D}^0}{2k_1 P} + \frac{k_\mathrm{A}\mathrm{P_A}}{2k_1}$$

and

$$P\cdot\mathrm{P_{O_2}} = \text{constant} + \frac{k_\mathrm{A}}{2k_1}P\cdot\mathrm{P_A}$$

where $\mathrm{P_{O_2}}$ and $\mathrm{P_A}$ are the partial pressures of O_2 and A respectively. For the stoichiometric mixture we have $\mathrm{P_{O_2}} = \frac{1}{3}P$ so that the final form of the equation is

$$P^2 = \text{constant} + \frac{3k_\mathrm{A}}{2k_1}P\cdot\mathrm{P_A} \qquad \text{(ii)}$$

Equation (ii) predicts that a plot of P^2 versus $P\cdot\mathrm{P_A}$ should be linear with gradient equal to $3k_\mathrm{A}/2k_1$: the data for the plot are as follows:

$10^{-6}P^2$ (Pa^2)	0·306	0·370	0·436
$10^{-3}P\cdot\mathrm{P_A}$ (Pa^2)	0	14·2	28·4

The plot is linear with gradient of $4{\cdot}58 = 1{\cdot}5k_\mathrm{A}/k_1$ so we have the result that $k_\mathrm{A}/k_1 = 3{\cdot}05$ at 898 K.

(*b*) The second explosion limit in the absence of added gases is determined by the ability of the termination reaction

$$\mathrm{H} + \mathrm{O_2} + \mathrm{M} \rightarrow \mathrm{HO_2} + \mathrm{M} \qquad (4)$$

(where M represents any molecule in the system) to balance the net propagation reaction, with the assumption that HO_2 radicals do not propagate the chain further. In the presence of B, an additional termination step is introduced and the explosion limiting condition is expressed by the equation

$$2k_1[\mathrm{H}][\mathrm{O_2}] = k_4[\mathrm{H}][\mathrm{O_2}][\mathrm{M}] + k_\mathrm{B}[\mathrm{H}][\mathrm{B}]$$

This can be rearranged to the form

$$[\mathrm{M}] = \frac{2k_1}{k_4} - \left(\frac{k_B}{k_4}\right)\left(\frac{[\mathrm{B}]}{[\mathrm{O}_2]}\right)$$

and applying the ideal gas law in the form $P = [\mathrm{M}]RT$ we obtain

$$P = \left(\frac{RT}{k_4}\right) 2k_1 - \frac{3k_B \mathrm{P_B}}{P}$$

taking into account that $\mathrm{P}_{\mathrm{O}_2} = P/3$ since the mixture is stoichiometric. Hence a plot of P versus the ratio $\mathrm{P_B}/P$ should be linear with a gradient to intercept ratio equal to $-3k_B/2k_1$. The data for the plot are

$10^{-3}P$ (Pa)	2·541	2·320	2·189	2·115
$10^4\mathrm{P_B}/P$	0	4·00	6·21	7·47

The plot is linear with gradient of $-5{\cdot}72 \times 10^5$ Pa and the intercept on the ordinate is $2{\cdot}54 \times 10^3$ Pa. Hence $3k_B/2k_1 = 5{\cdot}72 \times 10^5/2{\cdot}54 \times 10^3 = 225$. Therefore $k_B/k_1 = 150$ at 733 K.

Example 17

Radical addition polymerisation, inhibition of polymerisation, kinetic chain length, induction time.

The free-radical addition polymerisation of acrylonitrile (AN) in dimethylformamide solution at 333 K has been initiated by the thermal decomposition of 2,2′-azoisobutyronitrile (AIBN), which provides two identical radicals (R·). Upon addition of the stable monoradical known as Banfield's radical (BR·), the polymerisation was totally inhibited until all of the BR· was consumed, as indicated by the gradual decolorisation of the solution during this induction period (t_i). For initial concentrations of [AIBN]=0·060 mol dm^{-3} and [AN]=4·0 mol dm^{-3}, t_i varied with the added concentration of BR· as follows:

t_i (min)	0	29·0	51·4	67·6
10^3[BR·] (mol dm^{-3})	0	1·50	2·66	3·50

In the experiment where BR· is absent, the fraction (p) of the initial [AN] converted to polymer varied with time (t) as follows:

10^2p	5·37	10·5	15·3
t (min)	10	20	30

On the basis that one BR· reacts with one R· to produce inactive products, calculate the average number of AN units in the polymer molecules formed in the initial stages of reaction in the absence of BR· on the assumptions that termination involves only the combination of two growing chains and that the chains are very long.

Source: Szafko, J. and Manczyk, K. (1978) *Die Makromolekulare Chemie*, **179**, p. 2719. (Poland)

Solution

The mechanism of this addition polymerisation can be written as

$$\text{AIBN} \xrightarrow{k_i} 2\text{R}\cdot \qquad \text{initiation}$$

$$\left.\begin{array}{rcl} \text{R}\cdot + \text{AN} & \xrightarrow{k_p} & \text{R(AN)}\cdot \\ \text{R(AN)}\cdot + \text{AN} & \xrightarrow{k_p} & \text{R(AN)}_2\cdot \\ \cdots & & \cdots \\ \text{R(AN)}\cdot_{n-1} + \text{AN} & \xrightarrow{k_p} & \text{R(AN)}_n\cdot \end{array}\right\} \quad \text{propagation}$$

$$\text{R(AN)}_n\cdot + \text{R(AN)}_m\cdot \xrightarrow{k_t} \text{polymer} \qquad \text{termination}$$

$$\text{R}\cdot + \text{BR}\cdot \longrightarrow \text{inert product} \qquad \text{inhibition}$$

This involves the usual assumption that the rate constants for propagation steps are independent of the length of the growing chain—which is often true to a good approximation, and especially when the chain length is substantial, since then most growth acts involve a radical centre at the end of a long molecule.

Let R_I be the rate of thermal decomposition of AIBN, in which case $2R_I$ will be the rate of generation of the active centres. In the induction period, an amount of R· is produced equal to the available amount of BR· so that the initial concentration of the latter, $[\text{BR}\cdot]_o$ is a measure of the integrated rate of production of R· in time t_i. If the chains are long and $[\text{BR}\cdot]_o \ll [\text{AIBN}]_o$, we can regard $R_I = k_i[\text{AIBN}]$ as constant throughout t_i to a good approximation and we can write the equation as

$$2R_I t_i = [\text{BR}\cdot]_o$$

so that a plot of t_i versus $[\text{BR}\cdot]_o$ should be linear and pass through the origin. The plot conforms to these predictions and the inverse of the gradient may be equated to $2R_I$; this leads to $R_I = 2{\cdot}59 \times 10^{-5}$ mol dm^{-3} min^{-1}.

In the absence of BR· but with the same initial concentration of AIBN, we can consider R_I to be constant with the above value. Thus the rate of generation of active centres will be $2R_I = 5{\cdot}18 \times 10^{-5}$ mol dm^{-3} min^{-1} and for presumed steady state conditions this will be equal to the termination rate.

The propagation rate will be defined by the equation

$$-\frac{d[\mathrm{AN}]}{dt}=k_{\mathrm{p}}\sum[\mathrm{R(AN)}_n\cdot][\mathrm{AN}]$$

where $\sum[\mathrm{R(AN)}_n\cdot]$ represents the sum of the concentrations of all growing chains with $n=0$ to $n=\infty$: [AN] is the concentration of monomer at time t. The parameter p is defined by the equation

$$p=1-\frac{[\mathrm{AN}]}{[\mathrm{AN}]_{\mathrm{o}}}$$

where $[\mathrm{AN}]_{\mathrm{o}}$ is the initial concentration of AN. Differentiating we obtain

$$\begin{aligned}\frac{dp}{dt}&=-([\mathrm{AN}]_{\mathrm{o}})^{-1}\frac{d[\mathrm{AN}]}{dt}\\&=([AN]_{\mathrm{o}})^{-1}k_{\mathrm{p}}\sum[\mathrm{R(AN)}_n\cdot][\mathrm{AN}]\\&=k_{\mathrm{p}}\sum[\mathrm{R(AN)}_n\cdot](1-p)\end{aligned}$$

Now $k_{\mathrm{p}}\sum[\mathrm{R(AN)}_n\cdot]$ will be constant for a constant initiation rate so that on collecting the variables and integrating we obtain

$$\int_0^p\frac{dp}{(1-p)}=-\ln(1-p)=k_{\mathrm{p}}\sum[\mathrm{R(AN)}_n\cdot]t$$

Thus a plot of $-\ln(1-p)$ versus t should be linear with gradient of $k_{\mathrm{p}}\sum[\mathrm{R(AN)}_n\cdot]$. The data for the plot are as follows:

$-\ln(1-p)$	0·0552	0·1109	0·1661
t (min)	10	20	30

The plot is linear and passes through the origin as required. The gradient is $5{\cdot}54\times10^{-3}\ \mathrm{min}^{-1}=k_{\mathrm{p}}\sum\ [\mathrm{R(AN)}_{\mathrm{n}}\cdot]$.

The initial average kinetic chain length (L) is defined as the ratio of the initial propagation rate (after the establishment of a steady state) which is $k_{\mathrm{p}}\sum[\mathrm{R(AN)}_n\cdot][\mathrm{AN}]_{\mathrm{o}}$, to the initiation rate ($5{\cdot}18\times10^{-5}$ mol dm^{-3} min^{-1}), which is justifiably taken as constant in view of the small magnitudes of p. Hence we have

$$L=\frac{5{\cdot}54\times10^{-3}\times4{\cdot}00}{5{\cdot}18\times10^{-5}}=428$$

Since termination is achieved by the joining together of two growing chains, the average number of AN units in the initially produced polymer will be $2\times428=856$.

Example 18

Cationic addition polymerisation, "living" polymer (approximation to), adiabatic calorimetry.

The cationic addition polymerisation of iso-butyl vinyl ether (IBVE) in methylene chloride solvent and initiated by tropylium hexachloroantimonate ($C_7H_7^+SbCl_6^-$) has been studied at 248 K using an adiabatic calorimetry technique. In an experiment with initial concentration of the salt (fully dissociated in solution) of $8{\cdot}01 \times 10^{-5}$ mol dm^{-3}, the concentration of IBVE varied as a function of time (t) as follows:

t (s)	0	2	4	5	6	7	8	10	12	14	16
10^2[IBVE] (mol dm^{-3})	7·88	7·54	6·64	5·89	5·00	4·25	3·58	2·69	2·06	1·60	1·31

On the basis that termination is known to be insignificantly slow under these conditions, show that the maximum gradient of a plot of ln [IBVE] versus t allows evaluation of the propagation rate constant and calculate the value, assuming it to be independent of the number of monomer units attached to the active centre.

Source: Bawn, C. E. H., Fitzsimmons, C., Ledwith, A., Penfold, J., Sherrington, D. C. and Weightman, J. A. (1971) *Polymer*, **12**, p. 119. (U.K.)

Solution

The mechanism of addition polymerisation induced by a cation (and on other occasions an anion) takes the form

$$X^+ + M \xrightarrow{k_i} XM^+ \qquad \text{initiation}$$

$$\left.\begin{array}{l} XM^+ + M \xrightarrow{k_p} XM_2^+ \\ \cdots\cdots\cdots \\ XM_{n-1}^+ + M \xrightarrow{k_p} XM_n^+ \end{array}\right\} \qquad \text{propagation}$$

where X^+ is the cation and M the monomer. The effective absence of termination makes this situation an approximation to the "living" polymer situation: however the true "living" polymerisation system has no termination operative at all so that polymerisation proceeds until a monomer–polymer equilibrium is established. The active centres remain and upon further addition of monomer polymerisation will restart. (For an example of a true "living" polymer see problem 43.)

Let the concentration of all propagating species be denoted as $[XM_n^+]$. In the absence of an effective termination process, this concentration (of active centres) can only be changed (increased) by the initiation process. Let the initial concentration of the salt added be C_0 and at time t this will be distributed between the forms X^+ and XM_n^+ as regards the X^+ produced by the complete dissociation of the salt. Hence we can equate

$$C_0 = [X^+]+[XM_n^+] \qquad \text{(i)}$$

The differential rate law will take the form

$$\frac{-d[M]}{dt} = k_i[X^+][M]+k_p[XM_n^+][M] \qquad \text{(ii)}$$

and we shall have also

$$-\frac{d[X^+]}{dt} = k_i[X^+][M] \qquad \text{(iii)}$$

Substituting (i) into (ii) we obtain the equation

$$\begin{aligned} -\frac{d[M]}{dt} &= \{k_i[X^+]+k_p(C_0-[X^+])\}[M] \\ &= (k_i-k_p)[X^+][M]+k_pC_0[M] \end{aligned} \qquad \text{(iv)}$$

Equation (iv) may be recast in the form

$$-\frac{\frac{d[M]}{[M]}}{dt} = -\frac{d\ln[M]}{dt} = (k_i-k_p)[X^+]+k_pC_0$$

which upon rearrangement yields the expression for $[X^+]$

$$[X^+] = -\frac{k_pC_0+\frac{d\ln[M]}{dt}}{k_i-k_p} \qquad \text{(v)}$$

On differentiation of equation (v) with respect to time we obtain

$$\frac{d[X^+]}{dt} = -\frac{\frac{d^2\ln[M]}{dt^2}}{k_i-k_p}$$

On substitution of this equation and equation (v) into equation (iii) we obtain

$$(k_p-k_i)^{-1}\frac{d^2\ln[M]}{dt^2} = k_i\left(k_pC_0+\frac{d\ln[M]}{dt}\right)[M](k_p-k_i)^{-1}$$

Thus if ln [M] is plotted against t, then at the point of maximum slope the

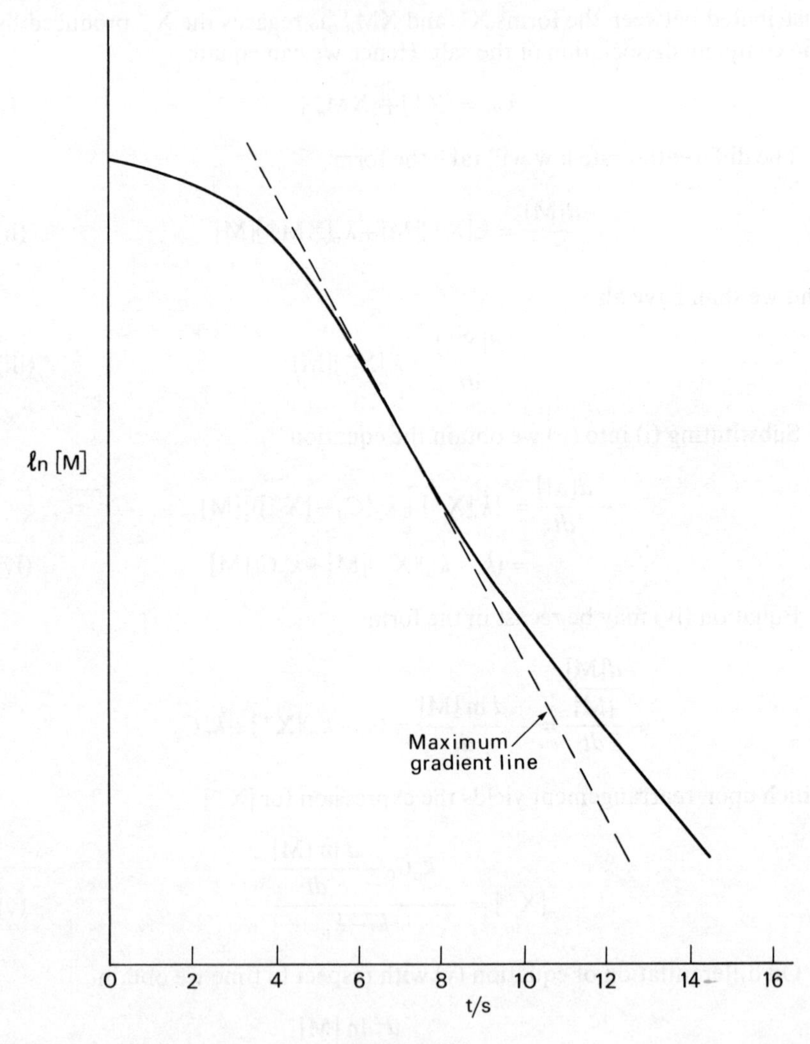

Figure 4.2

second differential $d^2 \ln [\mathrm{M}]/dt^2$ becomes zero and the above equation reduces to the simple form

$$-\left(\frac{d \ln [\mathrm{M}]}{dt}\right)_{\max} = k_p C_0$$

Therefore we plot ln [M] against t, for which the data are as follows

ln (10^2[M])	2·064	2·020	1·893	1·773	1·609	1·447
t (s)	0	2	4	5	6	7
ln (10^2[M])	1·275	0·990	0·723	0·470	0·270	
t (s)	8	10	12	14	16	

The form of the plot is shown in figure 4.2. The maximum slope is clearly defined for t between 5 and 8 s and is evaluated as

$$-0{\cdot}173\ \mathrm{s}^{-1} = -k_p C_0$$
$$= -8{\cdot}01 \times 10^{-5} k_p$$

so that $k_p = 2{\cdot}16 \times 10^3\ \mathrm{dm^3\ mol^{-1}\ s^{-1}}$.

Note: The fact that termination proceeds at an insignificant rate in comparison with initiation and propagation in this instance is of no general significance. In most cases termination is a significant process and must be taken account of in the analysis of the kinetics.

SECTION FIVE

COLLISION THEORIES OF REACTION KINETICS

Example 19

Lindemann theory of gas phase unimolecular reactions, thermal activation, steady state approximation, competitive reactions.

Ditertiarybutyl peroxide (DTBP) vapour has been thermally decomposed in the presence of nitric oxide producing tertiarybutyl nitrite (TBN) and acetone (Ac). The ratio of the initial rates (R) of formation of these products has been measured at 407 K as a function of the initial concentrations of DTBP and NO as follows:

10^3[NO] (mol dm^{-3})	0·49	0·34	0·23	0·14
10^3[DTBP] (mol dm^{-3})	1·57	1·09	0·75	0·45
R_{TBN}/R_{Ac}	13·5	11·9	10·5	9·66

The mechanism is known to be as follows:

$$\text{DTBP} \rightarrow 2\ \text{t-BuO}\cdot \qquad (1)$$

$$\text{t-BuO}\cdot + \text{M} \rightarrow \text{t-BuO}^{*}_{\cdot} + \text{M} \qquad (2)$$

$$\text{t-BuO}^{*}_{\cdot} + \text{M} \rightarrow \text{t-BuO}\cdot + \text{M} \qquad (3)$$

$$\text{t-BuO}^{*}_{\cdot} \rightarrow \text{CH}_3\cdot + \text{Ac} \qquad (4)$$

$$\text{t-BuO}\cdot + \text{NO} \rightarrow \text{TBN} \qquad (5)$$

where t-BuO· represents a tertiarybutoxyl radical having insufficient energy to decompose and t-BuO$^{*}_{\cdot}$ is the radical possessing sufficient energy to decompose in step (4).

Show that the above results conform with the predictions of the Lindemann theory for the unimolecular decomposition of tertiarybutoxyl radicals. Calculate the values at 407 K of the limiting first and second order rate constants for the thermal decomposition of t-BuO· radicals assuming that

only DTBP is effective as M in reactions (2) and (3), given that $k_5 = 3{\cdot}0 \times 10^7$ dm^3 mol^{-1} s^{-1} at 407 K.
Source: Yee Quee, M. J. and Thynne, J. C. J. (1967) *Transactions of the Faraday Society*, **63**, p. 2970. (U.K.)

Solution

The t-BuO· radical is generated by the thermal decomposition of DTBP, but the kinetics of this reaction (1) are of no consequence for the measured ratio of rates of formation of products, as will be apparent below. Once formed, the t-BuO· radical is removed by competitive processes—either thermal decomposition represented by steps (2), (3) and (4) in concert, or combination with NO to form the stable product TBN. Thus a measurement of the relative yields of the characteristic products Ac and TBN, respectively, after a certain extent of the reaction provides information on the relative effectiveness of the two routes of removal. Step (2) represents thermal activation of the t-BuO· radical, where it gains the energy requirement for decomposition by kinetic energy transfer in collisions with M, the other molecules in the system, which will have the normal Maxwellian distribution of velocities. (It may be noted at this stage that molecules can also be activated for decomposition by photochemical means (see example 20) or through formation of an energised molecule in a chemical reaction (see problem 44).

In analysis of the given mechanism, we may apply the steady state approximation to t-BuO*, which is expected to fall within the definition of a highly reactive intermediate species. Equating the rates of formation and removal of this species we obtain

$$k_2[\text{t-BuO}\cdot][\text{M}] = k_3[\text{t-BuO}^*][\text{M}] + k_4[\text{t-BuO}^*]$$

which rearranges to yield

$$[\text{t-BuO}^*] = \frac{k_2[\text{t-BuO}\cdot][\text{M}]}{k_3[\text{M}] + k_4} \qquad \text{(i)}$$

The rate of formation of acetone is given as

$$R_{\text{Ac}} = k_4[\text{t-BuO}^*] = \frac{k_2 k_4[\text{t-BuO}\cdot][\text{M}]}{k_3[\text{M}] + k_4} \qquad \text{(ii)}$$

The competitive rate of formation of TBN is given as

$$R_{\text{TBN}} = k_5[\text{t-BuO}\cdot][\text{NO}] \qquad \text{(iii)}$$

Combination of equations (ii) and (iii) yields the ratio of rates

$$\frac{R_{TBN}}{R_{Ac}} = \frac{k_5[NO](k_3[M]+k_4)}{k_2k_4[M]}$$

$$= [NO]\left(\frac{k_5k_3}{k_2k_4} + \frac{k_5}{k_2}[M]^{-1}\right) \qquad \text{(iv)}$$

Thus this predicts a linear plot of $R_{TBN}/R_{Ac}[NO]$ versus $[M]^{-1}$, where M is identified as DTBP on the basis of the given information that it is the only effective donor/acceptor of energy in reactions (2) and (3). Thus the data for the plot are as follows:

$10^{-4}R_{TBN}(R_{Ac}[NO])^{-1}$ ($dm^3\ mol^{-1}$)	2·76	3·50	4·57	6·90
$[M]^{-1}=[DTBP]^{-1}$ ($dm^3\ mol^{-1}$)	637	917	1330	2220

The plot is linear: the intercept is $1{\cdot}1 \times 10^4\ dm^3\ mol^{-1} = k_5k_3/k_2k_4$ and the gradient is $26 = k_5/k_2$, with the identification made from equation (iv).

Now steps (2), (3) and (4) are simply those of the Lindemann theory of unimolecular reactions: in isolation they would yield equation (i) on steady state analysis and therefore equation (ii) can be regarded as the Lindemann expression for the unimolecular decomposition rate. As $[M] \rightarrow \infty$ we expect equation (ii) to tend towards first order kinetics ($k_3[M] \gg k_4$) with a limiting first order rate constant denoted $k(\infty) = k_2k_4/k_3$. From the intercept of the above plot $k_5k_3/k_2k_4 = 1{\cdot}1 \times 10^4\ dm^3\ mol^{-1}$ and since k_5 is given as $3{\cdot}0 \times 10^7\ dm^3\ mol^{-1}\ s^{-1}$ we shall have

$$k(\infty) = \frac{3{\cdot}0 \times 10^7}{1{\cdot}1 \times 10^4}$$

$$= 2{\cdot}7 \times 10^3\ s^{-1} \qquad \text{for 407 K.}$$

As $[M] \rightarrow 0$, equation (ii) tends toward limiting second order kinetics ($k_4 \gg k_3[M]$) and the limiting second order rate constant is simply k_2. From the gradient of the above plot we have $k_5/k_2 = 26$ and with $k_5 = 3{\cdot}0 \times 10^7\ dm^3\ mol^{-1}\ s^{-1}$ we derive

$$k(0) = k_2 = \frac{3{\cdot}0 \times 10^7}{26}$$

$$= 1{\cdot}2 \times 10^6\ dm^3\ mol^{-1}\ s^{-1}$$

(It should be noted that it is the small range of [M] here which allows the Lindemann theory to provide an apparently adequate interpretation. However over a wider range of [M] significant deviations would be found and to attempt to interpret the results more rigorously, the workers applied a Lindemann–Hinshelwood treatment which took account of internal energy modes.)

Example 20

Unimolecular gas phase reaction, photochemical activation, Lindemann theory (deviation from), bimolecular collision frequency, collision cross-section, photodissociation.

The photodissociation of pure diazo-n-propane ($CH_3CH_2CHN_2$) vapour with the mercury lamp radiation transmitted by Pyrex glass ($\lambda > 300$ nm) yields products derived from the initially-formed, vibrationally-excited propylene molecule (Pr*), viz. propylene resulting from collisional stabilisation (referred to as S) and decomposition products, collectively referred to as D (e.g. ethylene, ethane). The variation of the ratio of D/S yields as a function of total pressure (P) was as follows for experiments conducted at 293 K with small conversions:

[D]/[S]	0·344	0·182	0·123	0·0854	0·0732	0·0452	0·0333
P (kPa)	0·123	0·330	0·664	1·07	1·33	2·26	3·06

(The components of D are such that one D molecule formed corresponds to one Pr* molecule decomposed.) It is known that Pr* is produced with a narrow range of energy (E) just in excess of the critical energy (E_o) for decomposition and, as a consequence, it may be assumed that Pr* is stabilised by every collision with another molecule.

(*a*) By plotting [D]/[S] against the appropriate function of P, show that these results deviate from the predictions of the Lindemann theory of unimolecular reactions.

(*b*) Explain in general terms how the results may be interpreted using a microscopic rate constant $k(E)$ for decomposition of Pr* which increases with E. If the collision cross-section for $Pr^* + CH_3CH_2CHN_2$ is 1·95 nm^2, calculate the average value of the rate constant for decomposition over the range of E produced, assuming thermal equilibrium for kinetic energy.

Source: Figuera, J. M., Fernandez, E. and Avila, A. J. (1974) *Journal of Physical Chemistry*, **78**, p. 1348. (Spain)

Solution

(*a*) The Lindemann theory view of this situation would be

$$Pr^* + M \xrightarrow{k_S} S + M \qquad (M = \text{diazo-n-propane})$$
$$Pr^* \xrightarrow{k_D} D$$

with the rate constants k_S and in particular k_D independent of the energy of Pr*. Hence on this basis and with application of the ideal gas law, the yield ratio will be given as

$$\frac{[D]}{[S]} = \frac{k_D}{k_S[M]} = \frac{RTk_D}{k_S P} \tag{i}$$

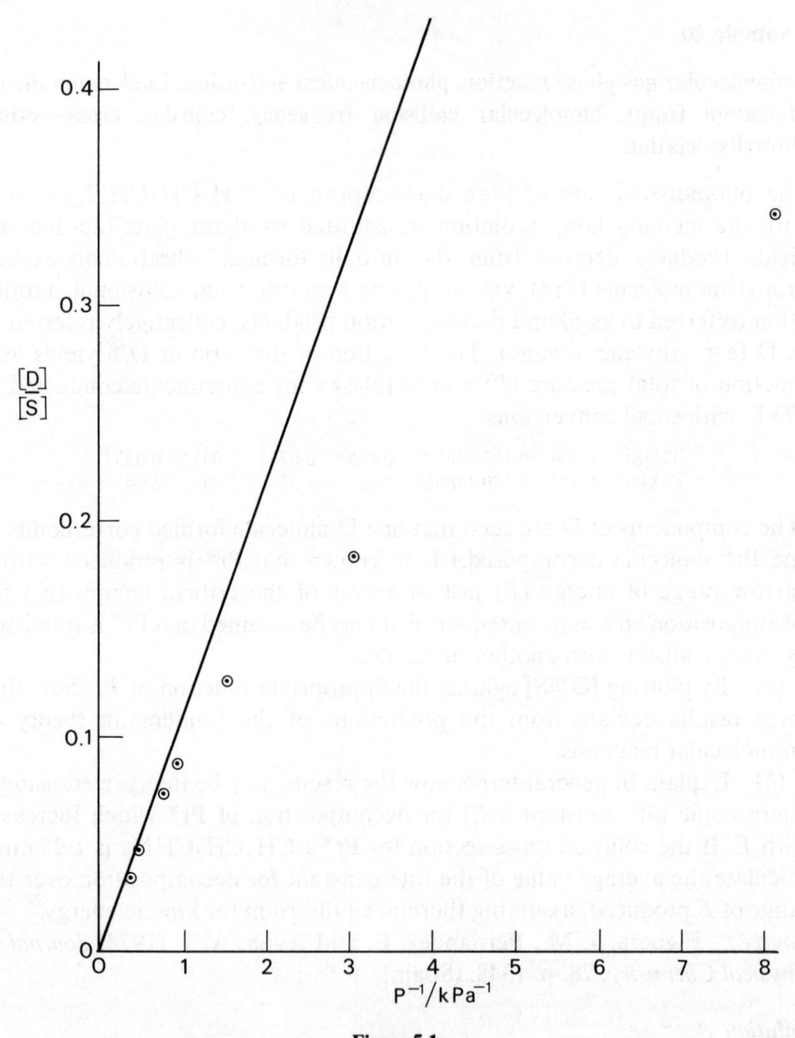

Figure 5.1

Thus the Lindemann theory considerations predict that the plot of [D]/[S] versus P^{-1} should be linear, for which the data are:

[D]/[S]	0·344	0·182	0·123	0·0854	0·0732	0·0452	0·0333
P^{-1} (kPa^{-1})	8·130	3·030	1·506	0·935	0·752	0·442	0·327

The plot is shown in figure 5.1. The plot is evidently not linear, with pronounced downward curvature towards the origin, so that the Lindemann theory predictions fail.

(*b*) If on the microscopic basis k_D is equated to $k(E)$, Z represents the collision number for $Pr^* + M$ and $f(E)$ is the fraction of Pr^* molecules having energy between E and $E+dE$, then under specified conditions the effective macroscopic (observable) value of k_D is simply the weighted average value of $k(E)$ over the energy range concerned ($E_o \rightarrow \infty$). The fraction of Pr^* molecules with a specified E which decompose is $k(E)/(k(E)+Z[M])$ and we may use this in the generation of the macroscopic value of k_D (denoted $\langle k_D \rangle$), through the usual averaging formula taking the particular form

$$\langle k_D \rangle = \frac{\displaystyle\int_{E_o}^{\infty} \frac{k(E)}{k(E)+Z[M]} f(E)\, dE}{\displaystyle\int_{E_o}^{\infty} \frac{1}{k(E)+Z[M]} f(E)\, dE} \qquad \text{(ii)}$$

If $k(E)$ increases with increasing E while Z is evidently constant, we can see that the $Z[M]$ term will have less effect the higher is E. In other words, a much higher [M], i.e. P, will be required to "quench" the decomposition pathway to a certain extent for higher E as opposed to lower E ($\geqslant E_o$). Thus as P increases, [D]/[S] decreases more rapidly for lower E than for higher E, and it is only at the highest P values (evidently from the plot where the lowest points can be approximately linearly-extrapolated to the origin) that it could be postulated that $Z[M]$ has become very much greater than $k(E)$ for all values of E concerned here. Under these limiting conditions, equation (ii) becomes

$$\langle k_D \rangle = \mathrm{Z[M]}^{-1} \int_{E_o}^{\infty} k(E) f(E)\, dE \Big/ \mathrm{Z[M]}^{-1} \int_{E_o}^{\infty} f(E)\, dE$$

and $(Z[M])^{-1}$ cancels out so that $\langle k_D \rangle$ becomes independent of pressure and is just the weighted average of $k(E)$ over the entire energy distribution by definition. The independence of $\langle k_D \rangle$ of P in the high pressure range then accords with the assumption of the Lindemann theory and produces the required linear plot of [D]/[S] versus P^{-1}.

Z can be calculated from the collision rate equation for an equilibrium distribution of kinetic energy

$$Z = \pi\sigma^2 \left(\frac{8kT}{\pi\mu}\right)^{1/2}$$

where $\pi\sigma^2 = 1{\cdot}95 \times 10^{-18}\ \mathrm{m}^2$ is the collision cross-section and k is the

Boltzmann constant. The reduced mass μ for relative molecular masses of 42 for Pr* and 70 for diazo-n-propane is given as

$$\mu = \frac{70 \times 42}{(70+42)6{\cdot}023 \times 10^{26}}$$
$$= 4{\cdot}36 \times 10^{-26}\ \text{kg}$$

The temperature T is 293 K so that we have

$$Z = 1{\cdot}95 \times 10^{-18}\left(\frac{8 \times 1{\cdot}38 \times 10^{-23} \times 293}{\pi \times 4{\cdot}36 \times 10^{-26}}\right)^{1/2}$$
$$= 9{\cdot}48 \times 10^{-16}\ \text{m}^3\ \text{molecule}^{-1}\ \text{s}^{-1}$$
$$= 5{\cdot}71 \times 10^{8}\ \text{m}^3\ \text{mol}^{-1}\ \text{s}^{-1}$$

For the highest pressure given, $P = 3{\cdot}06$ kPa, $[\text{M}] = 1{\cdot}26$ mol m^{-3} and hence $Z[\text{M}] = 5{\cdot}71 \times 10^8 \times 1{\cdot}26 = 7{\cdot}2 \times 10^8\ \text{s}^{-1} \equiv k_\text{S}$. Now since $[\text{D}]/[\text{S}] = \langle k_\text{D}\rangle / k_\text{S}[\text{M}] = 0{\cdot}0333$, we evaluate $\langle k_\text{D}\rangle = 0{\cdot}0333 \times 7{\cdot}2 \times 10^8 = 2{\cdot}4 \times 10^7\ \text{s}^{-1}$, considerably less than $Z[\text{M}]$ as required for this treatment.

Example 21

Termolecular reaction, Arrhenius equation, activation energy (negative), third body efficiencies in combination reactions.

Rates of removal of oxygen atoms in the presence of molecular oxygen and at large dilution in an inert gas, M, have been measured to yield rate constants ($_3k$) for the termolecular combination reaction:

$$\text{O} + \text{O}_2 + \text{M} \rightarrow \text{O}_3 + \text{M}$$

The following values of $_3k$ as a function of temperature (T) were measured:

T (K)	213	298	335	386
M = Ar				
$10^{-8}\,{}_3k$ (dm^6 mol^{-2} s^{-1})	5·39	1·86	1·38	1·01
M = CO_2				
$10^{-8}\,{}_3k$ (dm^6 mol^{-2} s^{-1})	34·9	12·0	8·96	6·55

(*a*) Show that these values of $_3k$ conform to the Arrhenius equation, exemplify the statement that the typical activation energy (E_a) for a termolecular combination reaction is between -4 and -10 kJ mol^{-1} and, when M is a small species, E_a is independent of the nature of M to a good approximation.

(*b*) If N_2 and O_2 have relative third body efficiencies of 1·5 and 1·1 respectively with respect to Ar as M in this reaction, calculate the rate of ozone formation by this reaction in the stratosphere at an altitude of 30 km

where $T = 227$ K, $[M] = 6{\cdot}4 \times 10^{-4}$ mol dm^{-3} (assume that the air is 20% O_2 and 80% N_2) and $[O] = 3{\cdot}0 \times 10^{-14}$ mol dm^{-3}.
Source: Mulcahy, M. F. R. and Williams, D. J. (1968) *Transactions of the Faraday Society*, **64**, p. 59. (Australia)

Solution
(*a*) The Arrhenius equation for $_3k$ will be

$$_3k = A \exp \frac{-E_a}{RT}$$

where A is the pre-exponential (frequency) factor and E_a the apparent activation energy. In logarithmic form this equation becomes

$$\ln {_3k} = \ln A - \frac{E_a}{RT}$$

Thus a linear plot of ln $_3k$ versus T^{-1} should be obtained if the given data are to conform to the Arrhenius equation with gradient equal to $-E_a/R$. The data for the plots for each M are as follows:

10^3K/T	4·69	3·36	2·99	2·59
M = Ar				
ln $(10^{-8}{_3k})$	1·685	0·6206	0·3221	0·0100
M = CO_2				
ln $(10^{-8}{_3k})$	3·553	2·485	2·193	1·880

The two plots are linear and form parallel lines with gradients of +795 K. Since this is to be equated to $-E_a/R$, we derive $E_a = -6{\cdot}61$ kJ mol^{-1}. Thus the statement made that the typical activation energy for this type of reaction is between -4 and -10 kJ mol^{-1} and is not significantly dependent on the nature of the third body M for small molecules is exemplified in both aspects.

(*b*) For M = Ar and $T = 227$ K, i.e. 10^3K/$T = 4{\cdot}41$, we read off the graph ln $(10_3^{-8}k/\text{dm}^6\ \text{mol}^{-2}\ \text{s}^{-1}) = 1{\cdot}46$ so that $_3k = 4{\cdot}31 \times 10^8$ dm^6 mol^{-2} s^{-1}. The relative third body efficiency for air will be the weighted average of those for N_2 and O_2, i.e. $(0{\cdot}80 \times 1{\cdot}5) + (0{\cdot}2 \times 1{\cdot}1) = 1{\cdot}42$ so that for M = air and $T = 227$ K, $_3k = 1{\cdot}42 \times 4{\cdot}31 \times 10^8 = 6{\cdot}12 \times 10^8$ dm^6 mol^{-2} s^{-1}.

The rate of ozone formation will be expressed through application of the Law of Mass Action to the elementary reaction as

$$\frac{d[O_3]}{dt} = {_3k}\,[O][O_2][\text{air}]$$

$$= 6{\cdot}12 \times 10^8 \times 3{\cdot}0 \times 10^{-14} \times 1{\cdot}3 \times 10^{-4} \times 6{\cdot}4 \times 10^{-4}$$

$$= 1{\cdot}5 \times 10^{-12}\ \text{mol dm}^{-3}\ \text{s}^{-1}$$

using $[air] = 6{\cdot}4 \times 10^{-4}$ mol dm^{-3}, $[O_2] = 0{\cdot}2[air] = 1{\cdot}3 \times 10^{-4}$ mol dm^{-3} and $[O] = 3{\cdot}0 \times 10^{-14}$ mol dm^{-3} as given.

(It is perhaps of interest to note that the reaction concerned here is only one of a set of processes involving ozone in the stratosphere, the individual rates of which combine to produce steady state concentrations of oxygen atoms and ozone.)

Example 22

Termolecular reaction—energy transfer mechanism, Principle of Microscopic Reversibility and Detailed Balancing, Lindemann mechanism of unimolecular reactions, flash photolysis.

The gas phase combination reaction of hydroxyl (OH) radicals with nitrogen dioxide in the presence of a large excess of nitrogen diluent

$$OH + NO_2(+N_2) \rightarrow HNO_3(+N_2)$$

has been studied using ultraviolet flash photolysis of nitric acid or water vapour as the source of OH in the presence of excess NO_2. The rate constants $_2k$ and $_3k$ are defined by the rate law

$$-\frac{d[OH]}{dt} = {}_2k[OH][NO_2] = {}_3k[OH][NO_2][N_2]$$

The experimental values of $_2k$ (with quoted error limit estimates of $\pm 18\%$) at varying $[N_2]$ and temperatures (T/K) were as tabulated below, with the limiting values calculated by an empirical procedure.

$10^3[N_2]$ (mol dm^{-3})	T(K) 220	296	550	
0·53	0·99	0·45		$10^{-9}\,{}_2k$ (dm^3 mol^{-1} s^{-1})
1·33	2·2	0·85		
2·66	3·9	1·6	0·19	
6·64	6·2	2·6	0·45	
13·3	8·1	4·0	0·64	
26·6	8·5	5·8		
$\rightarrow \infty$	12	9·6	2·7	
$\rightarrow 0$	2·3	0·87	0·22	$10^{-12}\,{}_3k$ (dm^6 mol^{-2} s^{-1})

Calculate the values of $_2k$ for each $[N_2]$ and T predicted by the simple energy transfer mechanism of termolecular combination reactions, presuming the limiting values to be exact. Specify the trend of the deviations of the measured values as a function of T: how might this be explained in general terms?

Explain how the energy transfer mechanism of the forward reaction above will be related to the Lindemann theory mechanism of the reverse reaction.

Source: Anastasi, C. and Smith, I. W. M. (1976) *Journal of the Chemical Society, Faraday Transactions II*, **72**, p. 1459. (U.K.)

Solution

The simple energy transfer mechanism will have the form

$$OH + NO_2 \underset{k_b}{\overset{k_a}{\rightleftharpoons}} HNO_3^*$$

$$HNO_3^* + N_2 \xrightarrow[k_c]{} HNO_3 + N_2$$

where HNO_3^* represents the weakly-bound complex possessing the energy required for redissociation. This is stabilised by transferring a small amount of this energy to N_2 in the last step, which is the rate-determining step for the eventual relaxation to a thermally-equilibrated HNO_3 molecule. We analyse the kinetics of this mechanism by application of the steady state approximation to the reactive (unstable) intermediate HNO_3^*; thus the formation and removal rates are equal

$$k_a[OH][NO_2] = (k_b + k_c[N_2])[HNO_3^*]$$

Rearrangement yields the expression for the steady state concentration

$$[HNO_3^*] = \frac{k_a[OH][NO_2]}{k_b + k_c[N_2]}$$

Now the rate-determining step for removal of OH will be that with rate constant k_c, so that the rate law takes the form

$$-\frac{d[OH]}{dt} = k_c[HNO_3^*][N_2] = \frac{k_a k_c[OH][NO_2][N_2]}{k_b + k_c[N_2]}$$

so that the experimental rate constant ${}_2k$ can be expressed as

$${}_2k = \frac{k_a k_c[N_2]}{k_b + k_c[N_2]} \qquad \text{(i)}$$

In the limit of $[N_2] \rightarrow \infty$ this will become ${}_2k(\infty)$ expressed as

$${}_2k(\infty) = k_a$$

At the same time the rate constant ${}_3k$ will be expressed as

$${}_3k = \frac{k_a k_c}{k_b + k_c[N_2]}$$

and in the limit of $[N_2] \rightarrow 0$ this will become ${}_3k(0)$ expressed as

$${}_3k(0) = \frac{k_a k_c}{k_b}$$

Hence on inverting both sides of equation (i) and making the substitutions we obtain

$$\begin{aligned} {}_2k^{-1} &= \frac{k_b}{k_a k_c[N_2]} + k_a^{-1} \\ &= {}_3k(0)^{-1}[N_2]^{-1} + {}_2k(\infty)^{-1} \end{aligned} \qquad \text{(ii)}$$

and on the basis of the limiting values given we have ${}_3k(O) = 2{\cdot}3 \times 10^{12}$, $8{\cdot}7 \times 10^{11}$ and $2{\cdot}2 \times 10^{11}$ $dm^6\ mol^{-2}\ s^{-1}$ at 220, 296 and 550 K respectively, and ${}_2k(\infty) = 1{\cdot}2 \times 10^{10}$, $9{\cdot}6 \times 10^9$ and $2{\cdot}7 \times 10^9$ $dm^3\ mol^{-1}\ s^{-1}$ at 220, 296 and 550 K respectively. Using these values in corresponding pairs in equation (ii) we calculate values of ${}_2k$ from the energy transfer (ET) theory to compare with those obtained experimentally (XP) in the table below, where the numbers given in the ET and XP columns are $10^{-9}\,{}_2k/dm^3\ mol^{-1}\ s^{-1}$ and Δ is the difference between them expressed as (ET − XP) × 100/XP (i.e. %).

				T(K)				
220			296			550		
ET	XP	Δ%	ET	XP	Δ%	ET	XP	Δ%
1·1	0·99	11	0·44	0·45	−2			
2·4	2·2	9	1·03	0·85	21			
4·1	3·9	5	1·9	1·6	19	0·48	0·19	152
6·8	6·2	10	3·6	2·6	38	0·95	0·44	116
8·7	8·1	7	5·3	4·0	33	1·4	0·64	119
10·1	8·5	18	6·8	5·8	17			

It is clear that, within the quoted error limit of ±18%, the energy transfer theory is quite adequate at 220 K, but the average deviations at the higher temperatures are too large to be explained within the error limits. The evident trend is for the average deviations to increase markedly with increasing temperature. In seeking a simple explanation, we may consider the internal energies of the reactants OH and NO_2 and the intermediate complex HNO_3^*, and in particular the vibrational energy contents. It is well known that vibrational energy modes are generally inactive at low temperatures, but can activate rapidly with increasing temperature: if this should occur from 220 K to 550 K for some of the vibrations involved here, then this would appear to be just the sort of effect we require. Since HNO_3^* should have 9 vibrational modes, it is reasonable to suppose that these might have a small energy content at 220 K and a rather more substantial energy content at 550 K for presumed thermal equilibrium. The present comparison of ET and XP values suggests that increasing activation of vibrational modes with increasing temperatures results in less rapid combination, when compared to the simple energy transfer mechanism: in general terms this could be regarded logically in terms of the higher internal energy content of HNO_3^* species being unhelpful to its stabilisation in subsequent collisions with N_2.

The Lindemann theory mechanism for the reverse unimolecular decomposition of HNO_3 would be written as follows:

$$HNO_3 + N_2 \rightleftarrows HNO_3^* + N_2$$
$$HNO_3^* \rightarrow OH + NO_2$$

and as such it is effectively the reverse of the energy transfer mechanism above. This is then in accord with the Principle of Microscopic Reversibility and Detailed Balancing view of this system, where the forward and reverse steps must follow the same detailed pathway, while the respective rate constants are always related through the equilibrium constant.

Example 23

Bimolecular (gas phase) collision theory, collision cross-section, "hot" atoms, Maxwell–Boltzmann distribution function, photodissociation.

Hydrogen atoms (ground electronic state only) have been produced with a range of initial kinetic energies at ambient temperature by photodissociation of hydrogen iodide gas with monochromatic radiation of various wavelengths between 342 nm and 248 nm. When nitrous oxide (N_2O) gas was present, the reaction with the "hot" hydrogen atoms was marked by nitrogen formation according to the equation

$$H^* + N_2O \rightarrow N_2 + OH$$

Measurements of the variation of N_2 yields as a function of the wavelength and conditions allowed evaluation of a parameter $p(E)$, which is the probability of reaction in a single collision involving total kinetic energy E (on average equally disposed in the three translational degrees of freedom), as follows:

$10^2\,p(E)$	0·17	0·52	1·3	2·1	2·2	2·0	1·2
E (kJ mol^{-1})	60	80	100	120	127	140	160

Estimate the value of the rate constant at 3000 K for the reaction between thermally-equilibrated H atoms and N_2O molecules on the assumption that relative kinetic energy in two dimensions alone drives the reaction, taking a collision cross-section of $0{\cdot}26\ nm^2$. Compare your answer with the rate constant of $6 \times 10^9\ dm^3\ mol^{-1}\ s^{-1}$ obtained experimentally for 3000 K. What factors could account for the difference?

Source: Oldershaw, G. A. and Porter, D. A. (1974) *Journal of the Chemical Society, Faraday Transactions I*, **70**, p. 1240. (U.K.)

Solution

The assumption is made that a collision between thermalised H and N_2O can only apply kinetic energy in two dimensions to overcoming the energy barrier to reaction (kinetic energy in the perpendicular direction to the collision plane is regarded as inapplicable on a simple bimolecular collisional basis).

The Maxwell–Boltzmann distribution function in two dimensions can be expressed as

$$\frac{dN}{N} = (kT)^{-1} \exp\left(\frac{-\epsilon}{kT}\right) d\epsilon$$

where ϵ is the energy of a particle and dN/N is the fraction of the total number N having energy between ϵ and $\epsilon + d\epsilon$ in two degrees of freedom. For a bimolecular collision this can be regarded as the probability of one of the colliding atoms or molecules having an energy between ϵ and $\epsilon + d\epsilon$ within the collision plane. When two particles collide, their kinetic energies within the collision plane are added to obtain the total kinetic energy available to promote reaction; thus the expression for the fraction of collisions involving a certain infinitesimal energy range has exactly the same form as above, since probabilities are multiplicative. Hence the fraction of collisions which involve a molar energy between E' and $E' + dE'$ in two dimensions can be expressed as:

$$\frac{dN}{N} = (RT)^{-1} \exp\left(\frac{-E'}{RT}\right) dE' = f(E')\, dE'$$

Now when a hot H atom collides with an N_2O molecule which is thermally-equilibrated at ambient temperature, the three dimensional energy E involved in the collision will be effectively the kinetic energy of the H atom. If E is on average equally disposed in three dimensions, then the average kinetic energy in two dimensions will be simply two thirds of E, i.e. $E' = \frac{2}{3}E$. Accordingly we can calculate values of the above function $f(E')$ for the values of E given as follows (with $T = 3000$ K):

E' (kJ mol^{-1})	40	53·3	66·7	80	84·7	93·3	106·7
$f(E')$ (mol kJ^{-1})	8·07(−3)	4·73(−3)	2·76(−3)	1·62(−3)	1·34(−3)	9·52(−4)	5·56(−4)
$p(E)$	1·7(−3)	5·2(−3)	1·3(−2)	2·1(−2)	2·2(−2)	2·0(−2)	1·2(−2)
$f(E')p(E)$ (mol kJ^{-1})	1·4(−5)	2·5(−5)	–	–	–	–	–

(The numbers in brackets are the indices of the multiplying powers of 10, e.g. 8·7(−3) = 8·7 × 10^{-3}.)

The reaction rate constant ($_2k$) for the bimolecular process proceeding at $T = 3000$ K will then be given by the integral of the product $f(E')p(E)$ over all energies, multiplied by the collision frequency. The simplest approach to the integration is to plot $f(E')p(E)$ versus E' and count the squares below the

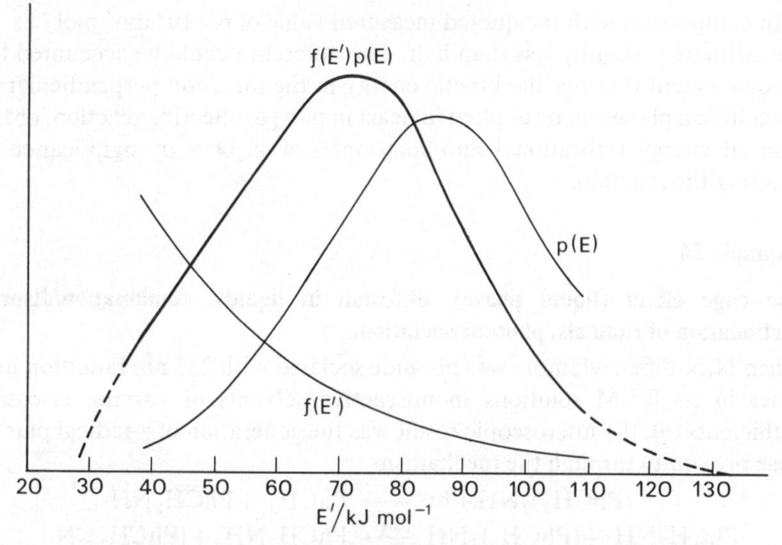

Figure 5.2

function to obtain the area enclosed. The plot has the form shown in figure 5.2.

We are forced to extrapolate this plot at both ends and therefore to make two reasonable assumptions derived from the trends which are discernible. Firstly we see that the value of the product $f(E')p(E)$ falls sharply as E' decreases towards 40 kJ mol^{-1}, and we can consider it to extrapolate to zero in the vicinity of $E' = 30$ kJ mol^{-1}. Secondly we see that both $f(E')$ and $p(E)$ are decreasing for $E' = 106{\cdot}7$ kJ mol^{-1} so that it is reasonable to consider the plot to extrapolate fairly smoothly to reach insignificant values of $f(E')p(E)$ in the vicinity of $E' = 140$ kJ mol^{-1}. On a scale where one small square on the graph paper corresponds to $0{\cdot}5 \times 2 \times 10^{-7}$, counting should produce around 18 500 small squares below the plot so that we obtain

$$\int_0^\infty f(E')p(E)\,dE' \simeq 18\,500 \times 1 \times 10^{-7} = 1{\cdot}9 \times 10^{-3}$$

The collision frequency Z is then calculated as shown in example 20, using $\pi\sigma^2 = 2{\cdot}6 \times 10^{-19}$ m^2 and reduced mass of the $H + N_2O$ collision system of $1{\cdot}64 \times 10^{-27}$ kg derived from relative masses of 1 for H and 44 for N_2O. Hence $Z = 2{\cdot}1 \times 10^{-15}$ m^3 molecule^{-1} s^{-1} $= 1{\cdot}3 \times 10^{12}$ dm^3 mol^{-1} s^{-1} is derived for $T = 3000$ K. Hence we shall have the final estimate of the rate constant

$$_2k = Z\int_0^\infty f(E')p(E)\,dE' = 1{\cdot}3 \times 10^{12} \times 1{\cdot}9 \times 10^{-3}$$

$$= 2{\cdot}5 \times 10^9 \text{ dm}^3 \text{ mol}^{-1} \text{ s}^{-1}$$

In comparison with the quoted measured value of 6×10^9 $dm^3\ mol^{-1}\ s^{-1}$, our estimate is slightly less than half. The difference could be accounted for to some extent if either the kinetic energy in the direction perpendicular to the collision plane can be applied (at least in part) to effecting reaction, or the internal energy (vibrational and rotational) of N_2O is of significance in effecting the reaction.

Example 24

The cage effect (liquid phase), diffusion in liquids, combination/disproportionation of radicals, photodissociation.

When N,N-dibenzylamine was photodissociated with 253 nm radiation in a series of its 0·5 M solutions in unreactive solvents of varying viscosity coefficients (η), the microscopic result was the generation of a radical pair in close proximity through the mechanism

$$(PhCH_2)_2NH + h\nu \longrightarrow PhCH_2\cdot + PhCH_2NH\cdot$$

$$PhCH_2NH\cdot + (PhCH_2)_2NH \xrightarrow{\text{fast}} PhCH_2NH_2 + (PhCH_2)_2N\cdot$$

The resultant benzyl ($PhCH_2\cdot$) and dibenzylamino ($(PhCH_2)_2N\cdot$) radicals underwent combination and disproportionation reactions forming the products $PhCH_3$, $(PhCH_2)_3N$, $(PhCH_2)_2$ and $PhCH{=}NCH_2Ph$. The ratios of the yields of toluene to bibenzyl for small extents of conversion were found to vary with η at constant ambient temperature as follows:

$10^2\eta$ (P)	0·208	0·362	0·606	0·778
$[PhCH_3]/[(PhCH_2)_2]$	3·8	4·9	6·3	7·0

On the assumption that the rates of diffusion of the radicals are proportional to the root mean square displacement in time t according to Brownian motion theory, show that these data are consistent with the operation of a cage effect in the solutions.

Source: Ratcliff, M. A. and Kochi, J.K. (1972) *Journal of Organic Chemistry*, **37**, p. 3275. (U.S.A.)

Solution

A cage effect will operate to tend to keep the initially-formed pair of radicals together, enclosed by a cage of solvent molecules: it is unlikely on a statistical basis that another dibenzylamine molecule will have been photodissociated within direct interaction range of the first. The only reactions occurring in the cage (examining the products) are

combination:

$$PhCH_2\cdot + (PhCH_2)_2N\cdot \rightarrow (PhCH_2)_3N$$

disproportionation:

$$PhCH_2\cdot + (PhCH_2)_2N\cdot \rightarrow PhCH_3 + PhCH{=}NCH_2Ph$$

Now if radicals escape from the cage by diffusion then they may react with radicals derived from other photodissociation acts, so that the additional reactions become possible

$$PhCH_2\cdot + PhCH_2\cdot \rightarrow (PhCH_2)_2$$

$$(PhCH_2)_2N\cdot + (PhCH_2)_2N\cdot \rightarrow (PhCH_2)_2NH + PhCH{=}NCH_2Ph$$

Thus bibenzyl can only be formed from benzyl radicals which have escaped from the cage, while toluene can be formed both within and outside the cage. It can be assumed that the radicals will react on a statistical basis once they have left the cage. Therefore the yield of bibenzyl must be determined by the rate of diffusion of benzyl radicals relative to their rate of reaction inside the cage.

We are told that the rate constant attaching to diffusion is proportional to the parameter r, the root mean square displacement in time t. Brownian motion (random walk) theory gives $r=(2Dt)^{1/2}$, where D is the relative diffusion coefficient for the radical pair. The Stokes–Einstein relationship then gives $D \propto \eta^{-1}$, so that if k_D is the effective rate constant for diffusion out of the cage, then we expect $k_D \propto r \propto D^{1/2} \propto \eta^{-1/2}$.

Reaction of the radical pair within the cage can be likened to that of an activated complex or transition state (see section 6) since the two are effectively "bound" to each other by the constriction of the cage, i.e. their reaction can be regarded as unimolecular and hence first order. The rate of diffusion apart of the radicals will also be first order in their effective (and equal) concentrations. Thus the ratio of the rate of reaction inside the cage to the rate of escape of the radicals must be inversely proportional to k_D, i.e. proportional to $\eta^{1/2}$. Once free from the cage, the radicals will combine statistically and we can expect the ratio of yields of toluene to bibenzyl formed *outside* the cage to be constant. But only toluene can be formed inside the cage and this yield will be proportional to $\eta^{1/2}$. Therefore we expect the ratio of total yields to be given by a relationship of the form

$$\frac{[\text{toluene}]}{[\text{bibenzyl}]} = A\eta^{1/2} + B$$

where A is a constant relating to the formation of toluene only within the cages and B is a constant relating to the statistical combination of escaped radicals. To test this prediction we plot the yield ratio against $\eta^{1/2}$ and the data for the plot are as follows:

$10^2\eta^{1/2}$ ($P^{1/2}$)	4·6	6·0	7·8	8·8
$[PhCH_3]/[(PhCH_2)_2]$	3·8	4·9	6·3	7·0

This plot is satisfactorily linear with a positive intercept on the ordinate, so that the data given are consistent with the operation of a cage effect.

Example 25

Diffusion-limiting rate constant (liquid phase), Fick's first diffusion law, encounter, half-life (second order reaction), steady state concentration, photodissociation, electron spin resonance detection.

The ultraviolet photolysis of low mol fractions of ditertiarybutyl ketone in solution leads to the formation of tertiarybutyl radicals (R·) through the mechanism

$$\mathrm{R-CO-R+h\nu \rightarrow R\cdot + RCO\cdot}$$
$$\mathrm{RCO\cdot \rightarrow R\cdot + CO}$$

Electron spin resonance detection can be used to measure the instantaneous concentration of R·. In an experiment conducted at 295 K with methylcyclopropane as solvent and continuous illumination, a steady concentration $[\mathrm{R\cdot}]=5{\cdot}48\times 10^{-7}$ mol dm^{-1} was measured. When the radiation was suddenly switched off, the half-life for decay of [R·] was 0·169 ms. Calculate the value of the rate constant ${}_2k$ at 295 K for the bimolecular process

$$\mathrm{R\cdot + R\cdot \rightarrow products}$$

which is considered solely responsible for the decay.

Relative values of ${}_2k$ for methylcyclopropane as solvent as a function of the viscosity coefficient (η) and temperature (T) are given below:

${}_2k$ (relative)	0·644	0·755	0·873	1·00	1·23
T (K)	265	275	285	295	313
$10^3\eta$ (P)	7·42	6·40	5·57	4·90	3·97

Show that these data are consistent with the rate of the above bimolecular process being controlled by diffusion of R· through the solvent, but not reacting at every encounter. Calculate the value of ${}_2k$ for the limiting case of infinitely fast diffusion.

Source: Schuh, H., Hamilton, E. J., Paul, H. and Fischer, H. (1974) *Helvetica Chimica Acta*, **57**, p. 2011. (Switzerland)

Solution

For a bimolecular reaction with two R· radicals as reactants and having a conventional rate constant ${}_2k$, the differential form of the rate law will be

$$\frac{-\frac{1}{2}\,d[\mathrm{R\cdot}]}{dt} = {}_2k[\mathrm{R\cdot}]^2$$

and this leads to the expression for the half-life (i.e. the time taken for the initial [R·] to decrease by a factor of two)

$$t_{1/2} = (2\,{}_2k[\mathrm{R\cdot}]_o)^{-1}$$

where $[R\cdot]_0$ is the initial concentration, which is $5{\cdot}48 \times 10^{-7}$ mol dm^{-3} in the present case when $t_{1/2} = 1{\cdot}69 \times 10^{-4}$ s. On substitution of these values into the above equation and rearranging we obtain

$$\begin{aligned} {}_2k &= (2 \times 1{\cdot}69 \times 10^{-4} \times 5{\cdot}48 \times 10^{-7})^{-1} \\ &= 5{\cdot}40 \times 10^{9}\ \text{dm}^3\ \text{mol}^{-1}\ \text{s}^{-1} \end{aligned}$$

On the basis of this absolute value for $T = 295$ K, we can convert all the other relative values of ${}_2k$ to absolute values, with the results below:

$10^{-9}\,{}_2k$ (dm^3 mol^{-1} s^{-1})	3·48	4·08	4·71	5·40	6·64
T (K)	265	275	285	295	313

The simplest theory of diffusion-limited reactions between uncharged species in solution regards reaction as occurring instantaneously when the two molecules first collide, i.e. encounter one another. Under these circumstances the concentration of a coreactant species (B) at the encounter distance (the sum of the molecular radii of the two reactants) from a reactant molecule (A) will be zero.

However, it is usually more realistic in the general case of a diffusion-limited reaction between molecules A and B to regard the concentration of B at the encounter distance as finite, say an average value of [B]*, but less than the bulk solution concentration of B at finite diffusion rates: this is equivalent to saying that reaction does not occur at every encounter. Fick's first diffusion law specifies the flux (F) of B molecules inwards through a spherical surface at distance r from the centre of an A molecule as

$$F = 4\pi r^2 D \left(\frac{d[\mathrm{B}]}{dr}\right)_r \qquad \text{(i)}$$

where D is the coefficient of relative diffusion, equal to the sum of the diffusion coefficients, $D_A + D_B$, for each species. Integration of equation (i) between the limits of the bulk concentration of B, denoted [B], at $r = \infty$ and [B]* at $r = r_{AB}$, the encounter distance, yields

$$\int_{r_{AB}}^{\infty} \frac{dr}{r^2} = \frac{4\pi D}{F} \int_{[\mathrm{B}]^*}^{[\mathrm{B}]} d[\mathrm{B}]$$

and hence we obtain

$$r_{AB}^{-1} = \frac{4\pi D}{F}([\mathrm{B}] - [\mathrm{B}]^*)$$

i.e.

$$[\mathrm{B}]^* = [\mathrm{B}] - \frac{F}{4\pi D r_{AB}} \qquad \text{(ii)}$$

At the same time we have the equation

$$F = {}_2k(\infty)[\mathrm{B}]^* \qquad \text{(iii)}$$

where ${}_2k(\infty)$ is a rate coefficient equal to the value of ${}_2k$ which would be observed if diffusion were infinitely fast, i.e. $[\mathrm{B}]^* = [\mathrm{B}]$. Substitution of equation (iii) into (ii) and rearrangement yields

$$[\mathrm{B}]^* = \frac{[\mathrm{B}]}{1 + \dfrac{{}_2k(\infty)}{4\pi D r_{\mathrm{AB}}}} \qquad \text{(iv)}$$

The observed rate constant for diffusion-limiting conditions will be

$${}_2k = \frac{\dfrac{d[\mathrm{A}]}{dt}}{[\mathrm{A}][\mathrm{B}]} = \frac{F}{[\mathrm{B}]}$$

since $-d[\mathrm{A}]/dt = F[\mathrm{A}]$.

Hence

$${}_2k = \frac{{}_2k(\infty)[\mathrm{B}]^*}{[\mathrm{B}]}$$

$$= \frac{4\pi D r_{\mathrm{AB}}}{1 + \dfrac{4\pi D r_{\mathrm{AB}}}{{}_2k(\infty)}} \qquad \text{from (iv).}$$

The Stokes-Einstein equation yields

$$D = \frac{Q_1 T}{\eta}$$

where Q_1 is a constant. Substitution into equation (iv) and noting that r_{AB} is also a constant, we predict the rearranged equation

$${}_2k^{-1} = \frac{Q_2 \eta}{T} + {}_2k(\infty)^{-1}$$

where Q_2 is another constant.

This prediction of a linear plot of the inverse of ${}_2k$ versus η/T should hold for our present system involving the R· + R· reaction, although it should be noted that the additional factor of $\frac{1}{2}$ appears in the rate law compared with the A + B case considered above, which will alter the value of Q_2: however the intercept will remain as ${}_2k(\infty)^{-1}$. The data for the plot are

$10^{10}\,{}_2k^{-1}$ (mol dm^{-3} s)	2·87	2·45	2·12	1·85	1·51
$10^5 \eta T^{-1}$ (PK^{-1})	2·80	2·33	1·95	1·66	1·27

The plot is linear confirming the diffusion control postulate. The ordinate intercept is $4{\cdot}0 \times 10^{-11}$ dm^{-3} mol s$= {}_2k(\infty)^{-1}$.

Hence the limiting value of ${}_2k$ for infinitely fast diffusion (i.e. ${}_2k(\infty)$) is $2{\cdot}5 \times 10^{10}$ dm^3 mol^{-1} s^{-1}.

(It may be noted that if reaction is regarded as taking place at every encounter, then we should require to set $[B]^* = 0$, but follow the same analytical procedure as above. Incorporation of the Stokes-Einstein equation in the explicit form

$$D_A = \frac{kT}{6\pi r_A \eta} \quad \text{and} \quad D_B = \frac{kT}{6\pi r_B \eta}$$

where r_A and r_B are the molecular radii, leads to the more familiar prediction that the diffusion-limiting value of ${}_2k$ (m^3 mol^{-1} s^{-1}) for reaction A+B is

$${}_2k = \frac{2RT}{3\eta} \frac{(r_A + r_B)^2}{r_A r_B}$$

where η is expressed in units of kg m^{-1} s^{-1} (1P$=0{\cdot}1$ kg m^{-1} s^{-1}). (This then predicts a direct proportionality between ${}_2k$ and T/η, which is clearly not applicable to the present data.)

SECTION SIX

THE TRANSITION STATE (ACTIVATED COMPLEX) THEORY OF REACTION KINETICS

Example 26

Unimolecular (gas phase) reaction, integrated first order rate law, Arrhenius equation, absolute rate theory, enthalpy of activation, entropy of activation, static constant volume reactor (measurement of pressure change).

The rate of thermal decomposition of pure perfluoro-di-tertiary butyl peroxide, $((CF_3)_3CO)_2$, vapour in a static constant volume quartz reaction vessel has been followed by measurement of the rate of change of total pressure. The only products of the reaction were C_2F_6 and CF_3COCF_3 with yields in the ratio 1:2 and the pressure at the end of reaction (P_∞) was three times the initial value (P_o). The pressures (P_t) at a set of times t after the start of reaction were measured and plots of ln $(P_\infty - P_t)$ versus t were found to be linear with gradients (G) as below, independent of P_o in the range 0·6 to 80 kPa, as a function of temperature, T:

T (K)	381	407	422
$-G$ (s^{-1})	$6{\cdot}5 \times 10^{-5}$	$1{\cdot}3 \times 10^{-3}$	$6{\cdot}3 \times 10^{-3}$

Derive values of the thermodynamic parameters of activation ($\Delta H^\ddagger$, $\Delta S^\ddagger$) for this reaction and the relationship of $\Delta H^\ddagger$ to the apparent Arrhenius activation energy, E_a.

The value of E_a for the thermal decomposition of ditertiary butyl peroxide, $((CH_3)_2CO)_2$, is approximately 150 kJ mol^{-1}, which is close to the dissociation energy of the peroxy (—O—O—) bond. What conclusions can be drawn on the mechanism of the decomposition of $((CF_3)_3CO)_2$?

Source: Ireton, R., Gordon, A. S. and Tardy, D. C. (1977) *International Journal of Chemical Kinetics*, **9**, p. 769. (U.S.A.)

Solution
It would be expected at the outset that the thermal decomposition kinetics would be first order, since this is a large molecule undergoing an initial unimolecular decomposition (likely to be the rate-determining step) and the rate constant is evidently independent of pressure.

The stoichiometric equation for the overall reaction can be written

$$((CF_3)_3CO)_2 \rightarrow C_2F_6 + 2CF_3COCF_3$$

from the given products and yields. Hence if C represents the concentration of reactant at time t then we can deduce

$$C \propto (P_\infty - P_t)$$

This becomes obvious when we examine the pressure relationships given and deriving from the stoichiometry

$$\frac{P_\infty}{3} = P_o \propto C_o$$

$$P_t = P_o + 2(P_o - \mathrm{P}_t)$$

where C_o is the initial concentration and P_t represents the partial pressure of reactant at time t.

Therefore $$P_\infty - P_t = 3P_o - P_o - 2P_o + 2\mathrm{P}_t = 2\mathrm{P}_t \propto \mathrm{C}$$

and $$P_\infty - P_o = 3P_o - P_o = 2P_o \propto C_o$$

The integrated first order rate law is

$${}_1kt = \ln\left(\frac{C_o}{C}\right) = \ln\left(\frac{P_\infty - P_o}{P_\infty - P_t}\right)$$

and for a particular experiment this means that

$$\ln(P_\infty - P_t) = -{}_1kt + \text{constant}$$

i.e. a linear plot as observed with the identification of the gradient G with $-{}_1k$ for a proven first order reaction.

For a unimolecular reaction, absolute rate theory expresses the rate constant, ${}_1k$, as

$${}_1k = e\left(\frac{kT}{h}\right)\exp\left(\frac{+\Delta S^\ddagger}{R}\right)\exp\left(\frac{-E_a}{RT}\right)$$

where k is the Boltzmann constant, h is Planck's constant, $\Delta S^\ddagger$ is the entropy of activation and E_a is the apparent Arrhenius activation energy, related to the enthalpy of activation, $\Delta H^\ddagger$, as $E_a = \Delta H^\ddagger + RT$ for a situation where there is no change in the number of molecules as the activated complex is formed from the reactant molecule.

Firstly we can make the usual Arrhenius plot of ln ${}_1k$ versus T^{-1}, when the gradient will be equal to $-E_a/R$. The data for the plot are as follows:

ln $({}_1k)$	$-9{\cdot}641$	$-6{\cdot}645$	$-5{\cdot}067$
10^3 K/T	2·625	2·457	2·370

The plot is linear with gradient $= -1{\cdot}79 \times 10^4$ K and hence $E_a =$ 149 kJ mol^{-1}.

The average temperature over the small range is 402 K so that we derive

$$\Delta H^{\ddagger} = E_a - RT$$
$$= 1{\cdot}49 \times 10^5 - 8{\cdot}314 \times 402 = 146 \text{ kJ mol}^{-1}$$

Also, using the middle result at 407 K, and the absolute rate theory equation given above with $k = 1{\cdot}38 \times 10^{-23}$ J molecule^{-1} K^{-1} and $h = 6{\cdot}63 \times 10^{-34}$ J s, we have the numerical form

$$1{\cdot}3 \times 10^{-3} = e(8{\cdot}47 \times 10^{12}) \exp\left(\frac{\Delta S^{\ddagger}}{R}\right) 7{\cdot}52 \times 10^{-20}$$

and upon rearrangement this yields

$$\exp\left(\frac{\Delta S^{\ddagger}}{R}\right) = 750$$

and hence

$$\Delta S^{\ddagger} = +55{\cdot}0 \text{ J mol}^{-1} \text{ K}^{-1}$$

This positive value of $\Delta S^{\ddagger}$ suggests that the transition state is produced by extension of one or more bonds with consequent increase in the degree of disorder. We note that the decomposition of ditertiary butyl peroxide involves almost the same E_a (~ 150 kJ mol^{-1}) as that derived above and, since this approximates to the dissociation energy of the peroxy bond, the clear implications are that the substitution of F for H at the ends of the peroxy molecule does not alter the dissociation energy of the —O—O— bond significantly, and that it is this bond which breaks in the initial step and is extended in the transition state. Thus the likely initial step can be represented as

$$(CF_3)_3CO\text{—}OC(CF_3)_3 \rightarrow 2(CF_3)_3CO\cdot$$

Although we have no direct evidence other than the nature of the products, we may strongly suspect that the subsequent (non-rate-determining) steps are

$$(CF_3)_3CO\cdot \rightarrow CF_3\cdot + CF_3COCF_3$$
$$CF_3\cdot + CF_3\cdot \rightarrow C_2F_6$$

It may be noted that the absolute rate theory always expresses the rate constant for an elementary reaction of order n as

$$ {}_nk = \frac{kT}{h}\exp\left(\frac{+\Delta S^{\ddagger}}{R}\right)\exp\left(\frac{-\Delta H^{\ddagger}}{RT}\right) $$

However for *gas* phase reactions, the relationship of $\Delta H^{\ddagger}$ to E_a depends on the molecularity, e.g. for a bimolecular reaction where two reactant molecules combine to form one entity in the transition state the relationship is

$$ E_a = \Delta H^{\ddagger} + 2RT $$

Example 27

Volume of activation, solvation effects, polarity effects, pressure effect on reaction rate, entropy of activation.

The rate of the oxidative reaction of "Vaska's compound" $IrCl(CO)(P(C_6H_5)_3)_2$ with methyl iodide at 298 K has been measured in the solvents toluene (TOL) and dimethylformamide (DMF) under varying applied pressures (P). The reaction was first order in each reactant and the rate constants, k_{TOL} and k_{DMF} in the respective solvents, were as below:

$10^{-2}P$ (kPa)	1·01	253	507	760	1013
k_{TOL} ($dm^3\ mol^{-1}\ min^{-1}$)	0·150	0·200	0·267	0·356	0·474
k_{DMF} ($dm^3\ mol^{-1}\ min^{-1}$)	1·70	1·98	2·32	2·71	3·16

Calculate the volumes of activation for this reaction in the two solvents.

Deduce the general nature of the transition state involved on the assumption that it is the same chemically for both solvents, taking into account that DMF is considerably more polar than toluene; explain in general terms the difference between the volumes of activation calculated.

Predict the sign of the entropy of activation of this reaction.

Source: Stieger, H. and Kelm, H. (1973) *Journal of Physical Chemistry*, **77**, p. 290. (West Germany)

Solution

The volume of activation of a reaction ($\Delta V^{\ddagger}$) is the volume change which takes place when the reactants form the transition state. In a solution reaction it can involve two components, the first reflecting the change in volume of the reacting molecules forming the transition state in isolation from the solvent, the second corresponding to the change in solvation during this process. The latter will clearly reflect the polarity (i.e. separation of charges) of the species involved, since to a large extent that determines the degree of solvation by a solvent of a particular polarity.

The variation of a rate constant at constant temperature with applied pressure is given by the differential relationship

$$\left(\frac{\partial \ln k_X}{\partial P}\right)_T = -\frac{\Delta V^\ddagger}{RT}$$

where k_X is the rate constant in solvent X. $\Delta V^\ddagger$ may be a slight function of P itself (just as $\Delta H^\ddagger$ may be a slight function of T): however the variation is usually small enough to be ignored so that the integrated form of the above equation is

$$\ln k_X(P) = \ln k_X(0) - \left(\frac{\Delta V^\ddagger}{RT}\right)P$$

where $k_X(P)$ is the rate constant at applied pressure P. Accordingly we shall plot the given values of $k_X(P)$ in the form of $\ln k_X(P)$ versus P, when a linear plot of gradient $-\Delta V^\ddagger/RT$ should result for each solvent. The data are:

$10^{-2}P$ (kPa)	1·01	253	507	760	1013
$\ln k_{TOL}$	−1·897	−1·609	−1·321	−1·033	−0·747
$\ln k_{DMF}$	0·531	0·683	0·842	0·997	1·150

Both plots are linear as required. The k_{TOL} plot has a gradient of $+1{\cdot}14 \times 10^{-5}$ kPa^{-1} $= 1{\cdot}14 \times 10^{-8}$ Pa^{-1}. Hence for toluene as solvent we derive $\Delta V^\ddagger = -1{\cdot}14 \times 10^{-8} \times 8{\cdot}314 \times 298 = -2{\cdot}82 \times 10^{-5}$ m^3 mol^{-1}.

The k_{DMF} plot has gradient of $+6{\cdot}12 \times 10^{-6}$ kPa so that $\Delta V^\ddagger = -6{\cdot}12 \times$ $\times 10^{-9} \times 8{\cdot}314 \times 298 = -1{\cdot}52 \times 10^{-5}$ m^3 mol^{-1}.

Thus we find that for the more polar solvent (DMF), the magnitude of $\Delta V^\ddagger$ is approximately half that for the less polar solvent, both being negative. On the face of it, negative values of $\Delta V^\ddagger$ would be expected for a situation where the transition state is formed by the conjunction of two separate reactants. However if the transition state is strongly polar, it will draw solvent molecules (dipoles) onto itself, which will also make a negative contribution to $\Delta V^\ddagger$ if the original volume is considered to include both the original reactants, their solvation molecules and the additional (initially free) solvent molecules solvated in the transition state. The argument then is that, for a highly polar transition state, the smaller the polarity of the solvent, the greater the change in solvation, as the solvent molecules themselves will be less strongly attracted towards one another. This is the trend observed here and in the absence of further information to separate the two components of $\Delta V^\ddagger$, all we can say is that the transition state is indicated to be strongly polar and is most likely formed by the addition of the two reactant molecules.

Since the degree of order achieved by a strongly solvated transition state will be high, we can predict that $\Delta S^\ddagger$ will be negative (see example 29 for the convention in this connection) in association with a negative $\Delta V^\ddagger$.

Example 28

Free energy of activation, Hammett relationship (free energy relationship), absolute rate theory, half-life of reaction.

The decyanoethylation of the compounds of general formula para-XC_6H_4—$C(CH_3)$=N—O—$(CH_2)_2CN$ (A) in the presence of aqueous NaOH proceeds according to the stoichiometric equation

$$A + OH^- \rightarrow \text{para-}XC_6H_4\text{—}C(CH_3)\text{=N—}O^- + CH_2\text{=CH—CN} + H_2O$$

At 298 K, with initial concentrations of A of approximately 5×10^{-5} mol dm^{-3}, the half-life ($t_{1/2}$) for the disappearance of A in NaOH solutions varied as below for different substituents (X):

X	CH_3O	CH_3	Br	NO_2
$t_{1/2}$ (min)	24·7	105	55·4	23·3
$[OH^-]$ (mol dm^{-3})	0·50	0·10	0·10	0·10

These $t_{1/2}$ values were independent of the initial concentration of A but increased in proportion to $[OH^-]^{-1}$ for a particular X.

Show that these results are consistent with the linear free energy (of activation) relationship expressed by the Hammett equation for a homologous series of para-substituted benzene reactants, given that the values of the parameter σ in the Hammett equation are as follows: $-0{\cdot}27$ for CH_3O, $-0{\cdot}17$ for CH_3, 0·23 for Br and 0·78 for NO_2, all as para-substituents. Predict the half-life of A with X=H in a solution at 298 K with $[OH^-]=$ 0·20 mol dm^{-3}.

Source: Buchwald, P. and Fey, L. (1975) *Revue Roumaine de Chimie*, **20**, p. 379. (Roumania)

Solution

The first point to note is that the $t_{1/2}$ measurements were made under conditions where $[A] \ll [OH^-]$. Since $t_{1/2}$ is independent of $[A]_o$ but varies inversely with $[OH^-]$, the reaction is evidently second order overall, first order in each reactant and occurring under pseudo-first order conditions here (see example 5 for a similar situation). The rate law is therefore

$$-\frac{d[A]}{dt} = {}_2k[A][OH^-]$$

$$= {}_1k[A] \qquad ({}_1k = {}_2k[OH^-])$$

Therefore the half-life is related to the pseudo-first order rate constant ${}_1k$ and the second order rate constant ${}_2k$ as follows:

$$t_{1/2} = \frac{0{\cdot}693}{{}_1k} = \frac{0{\cdot}693}{{}_2k\,[OH^-]}$$

and we can evaluate values of ${}_2k$ from the given $t_{1/2}$ data as follows:

X =	CH_3O	CH_3	Br	NO_2
$10^2{}_1k$ (min^{-1})	2·81	0·660	1·25	2·97
$[OH^-]$ (mol dm^{-3})	0·50	0·10	0·10	0·10
$10^4{}_2k$ (dm^3 mol^{-1} s^{-1}	9·4	11	21	50

Now absolute rate theory expresses the rate constant as

$${}_2k = \frac{kT}{h} \exp\left(-\frac{\Delta G^{\ddagger}}{RT}\right)$$

(c.f. note at end of example 26) and hence we shall have

$$\ln {}_2k = \text{constant} - \frac{\Delta G^{\ddagger}}{RT} \qquad \text{(i)}$$

In developing the Hammett equation, it is postulated that for a series of para-substituted reactants (as here) there is a linear relationship expressed as

$$\Delta G^{\ddagger} = \Delta G^{\ddagger}_{\text{o}} - RT\rho\sigma$$

Of the two parameters, σ is characteristic of the nature of the para-substituent while ρ is effectively a reaction constant, varying with the reaction and the external conditions. $\Delta G^{\ddagger}_{\text{o}}$ is the free energy of activation for X=H, for which $\sigma=0$ by convention. Thus equation (i) may be expressed as the Hammett equation written as

$$\ln {}_2k_{\text{X}} = \ln {}_2k_{\text{H}} + \sigma_{\text{X}}\rho$$

where the subscripts denote the substituent. Therefore, if the given data are to conform to this equation, a linear plot for $\ln {}_2k_{\text{X}}$ versus σ_{X} should result. The data for the plot are as follows:

$\ln(10^4{}_2k)$	2·241	2·398	3·045	3·912
σ_{X}	−0·27	−0·17	0·23	0·78

The graph is linear as required since ρ will be a constant for this particular reaction under the specified conditions.

Also at $\sigma_{\text{X}}=0$ we read off $\ln(10^4{}_2k/\text{dm}^3\ \text{mol}^{-1}\ \text{s}^{-1})=2{\cdot}672$ so that ${}_2k_{\text{H}}=1{\cdot}4\times10^{-3}$ dm^3 mol^{-1} s^{-1}m for X=H. With $[OH^-]=0{\cdot}20$ mol dm^{-3}, this leads to the pseudo-first order rate constant for X=H of ${}_1k=2{\cdot}8\times10^{-4}$ $s^{-1}=1{\cdot}7\times10^{-2}$ min^{-1}. Hence $t_{1/2}=0{\cdot}693/1{\cdot}7\times10^{-2}=40$ min.

(Hammett's equation applies quite accurately to a substantial number of rate constants and is therefore of value for the prediction of rate constants from a small number of values of σ and ρ. The Hammett equation does not apply very well to reactions of aliphatic compounds, but a rather similar relationship, known as the Taft equation, has been found to hold there.)

Example 29

Entropy of activation (ionic reaction in solution), absolute rate theory, Arrhenius equation, activation energy, solvation effects, pseudo-order reaction, stopped-flow system, Law of Mass Action.

The redox reaction, for which the stoichiometric equation is

$$V(H_2O)_6^{2+} + Ru(NH_3)_6^{3+} \rightarrow V(H_2O)_6^{3+} + Ru(NH_3)_6^{2+}$$

has been studied in a stopped-flow system under conditions where the concentration of $V(H_2O)_6^{2+}$ was more than 10 times that of $Ru(NH_3)_6^{3+}$. From absorbance measurements at a wavelength of 275 nm (where the vanadium species are transparent) in solutions of constant ionic strength (adjusted with perchloric acid), the decay of $[Ru(NH_3)_6^{3+}]$ was found to follow first order kinetics and the apparent rate constant, ${}_1k$, had the values below as a function of $[V(H_2O)_6^{2+}]$ and temperature (T):

${}_1k$ (s^{-1})	0·232	2·03	5·59	0·394	1·75	5·46
$10^4\,[V(H_2O)_6^{2+}]$ (mol dm^{-3})	2·00	17·5	48·0	2·70	12·0	37·3
T (K)	285·8			317·8		

Show that these data indicate an elementary nature for the above redox reaction. Calculate the entropy of activation ($\Delta S^{\ddagger}$) and explain its sign (on a basis where $\Delta S^{\ddagger}=0$ corresponds to an Arrhenius pre-exponential factor approximating to the gas phase collision frequency for uncharged species).
Source: Jacks, C. A. and Bennett, L. E. (1974) *Inorganic Chemistry*, **13**, p. 2035. (U.S.A.)

Solution
If the reaction is to be elementary then, on the basis of the stoichiometric equation and application of the Law of Mass Action, it must be bimolecular and hence show second order kinetics. Using Ru to denote $Ru(NH_3)_6^{3+}$ and V to denote $V(H_2O)_6^{2+}$ (i.e. the reactants) the rate law will be

$$-\frac{d[Ru]}{dt} = {}_2k[Ru][V] = {}_1k[Ru]$$

where ${}_2k$ is the bimolecular rate constant and ${}_1k$ is the pseudo-first order rate constant reflecting the fact that $[V] \gg [Ru]$. Hence ${}_1k$ here is identified as the observed rate constant, so that ${}_1k/[V] = {}_2k$ should be constant for a particular temperature (T). Taking the results in the given order, we calculate apparent values of ${}_2k$ as follows:

$10^{-3}\,{}_2k$ (dm^3 mol^{-1} s^{-1})	1·16	1·16	1·16	1·46	1·46	1·46
T (K)	285·8			317·8		

The constancy of ${}_2k$ for each temperature indicates a second order reaction, which would be consistent with an elementary, bimolecular nature.

For a bimolecular reaction in solution, absolute rate theory predicts

$$
\begin{aligned}
{}_2k &= \left(\frac{kT}{h}\right)\exp\left(+\frac{\Delta S^\ddagger}{R}\right)\exp\left(-\frac{\Delta H^\ddagger}{RT}\right) \\
&= e\left(\frac{kT}{h}\right)\exp\left(+\frac{\Delta S^\ddagger}{R}\right)\exp\left(-\frac{E_a}{RT}\right)
\end{aligned}
$$

where $\Delta S^\ddagger$ is the entropy of activation, $\Delta H^\ddagger$ is the enthalpy of activation and E_a is the apparent Arrhenius activation energy. For all molecularities of reactions in solution, the relationship $E_a = \Delta H^\ddagger + RT$ holds since the work of compression in forming the transition state is negligible (i.e. $\Delta U = \Delta H$ in the liquid phase). On the basis of the Arrhenius equation we shall have

$$\ln\left(\frac{{}_2k(T_1)}{{}_2k(T_2)}\right) = -\frac{E_a}{R}(T_1^{-1} - T_2^{-1})$$

where ${}_2k(T)$ denotes the rate constant at temperature T. On rearrangement and incorporation of the values, ${}_2k(285{\cdot}8) = 1{\cdot}16 \times 10^3\ \mathrm{dm^3\ mol^{-1}\ s^{-1}}$ for $T = 285{\cdot}8$ K and ${}_2k(317{\cdot}8) = 1{\cdot}46 \times 10^3\ \mathrm{dm^3\ mol^{-1}\ s^{-1}}$ for $T = 317{\cdot}8$ K, we obtain the expression for the activation energy

$$E_a = -\ln\left(\frac{1{\cdot}46}{1{\cdot}16}\right)\frac{R}{317{\cdot}8^{-1} - 285{\cdot}8^{-1}} = 5{\cdot}43\ \mathrm{kJ\ mol^{-1}}$$

Hence taking this value in conjunction with say the result at $T = 285{\cdot}8$ K we can use the absolute rate theory expression above to evaluate $\Delta S^\ddagger$, the only unknown. However we are told to use a basis where $\Delta S^\ddagger = 0$ would approximate to an Arrhenius pre-exponential factor of the order of the bimolecular gas phase collision frequency for uncharged species: on this basis the absolute rate theory expression implies that $e(kT/h)$ should approximate to this collision frequency. At $T \simeq 300$ K, $e(kT/h)$ evaluates as $\sim 2 \times 10^{13}\ \mathrm{s^{-1}}$, so that the numerical value of the frequency factor of ${}_2k$ should be of this order. It turns out that the collision frequency of gas phase species is approximately 10^{14} when expressed in units of $\mathrm{cm^3\ mol^{-1}\ s^{-}}$ (see example 20): it is then sufficiently accurate for present purposes to say that if ${}_2k$ in the absolute rate theory expression is put in units of $\mathrm{cm^3\ mol^{-1}\ s^{-1}}$, then $\Delta S^\ddagger$ will be evaluated with a meaningful sign. Thus with ${}_2k = 1{\cdot}16 \times 10^6$ $\mathrm{cm^3\ mol^{-1}\ s^{-1}}$ for $T = 285{\cdot}8$ K and the absolute rate theory expression in logarithmic form we have the equation

$$\ln(1{\cdot}16 \times 10^6) = 1 + \ln\left(\frac{kT}{h}\right) + \frac{\Delta S^\ddagger}{R} - \frac{E_a}{RT}$$

$$13{\cdot}9639 = 1 + 29{\cdot}4150 + \frac{\Delta S^\ddagger}{R} - 2{\cdot}2852$$

so that

$$\Delta S^{\ddagger} = R(-14{\cdot}17) = -118 \text{ J mol}^{-1} \text{ K}^{-1}$$

This reaction has therefore a transition state which represents a considerable increase in order compared to the separate reactants. Since the transition state will have a charge of $+2+3=+5$ concentrated in a smaller volume than that for the separate reactants, the increase in order can be regarded in terms of the increased solvation likely to be associated with the more concentrated charge of the transition state. This is the typical situation for reactions between ions of like charges. For reactions between ions of opposite charges, exactly the reverse argument applies and the typical $\Delta S^{\ddagger}$ is positive on the basis of the above convention.
(A thorough discussion of the apparent problems with the dimensions and standard states in activated complex theory has been given by Robinson, P. J. (1978) *Journal of Chemical Education*, **55**, p. 509.)

Example 30

Primary kinetic salt effect, Bronsted–Bjerrum equation, electrical conductivity measurements in solution.

The electrical conductivity of solutions of triphenyl(methyl) stibonium bromide $[(C_6H_5)_3SbCH_3^+Br^-]$ in acetonitrile (unionised solvent) at 298 K has been found to decrease with time due to decomposition represented

$$(C_6H_5)_3SbCH_3^+Br^- \rightarrow (C_6H_5)_3Sb + CH_3Br$$

where the products are non-conducting. The initial rates of change of conductivity (R_c) as a function of the initial concentration of reactant (C_o) were as below, together with values for the initial conductance (X) and the degree of dissociation (α) of the reactant:

$10^9 R_c$ (ohm^{-1} s^{-1})	1·596	0·7961	0·2882	0·1095
$10^3 C_o$ (mol dm^{-3})	5·987	3·085	1·462	0·7803
$10^4 X$ (ohm^{-1})	36·25	22·46	12·16	7·041
α	0·633	0·737	0·821	0.872

Interpret these results on the basis of a bimolecular reaction with the separated ions as the reactants, using the Debye–Huckel theory expression for the activity coefficient of an ion in solution of ionic strength I. Evaluate the limiting value of the bimolecular rate constant for $I \rightarrow 0$.
Source: Parris, G. E., Long, G. G., Andrews, B. C., and Parris, R. M., (1976), *Journal of Organic Chemistry*, **41** p. 1276. (U.S.A.)

Solution

If we represent the reactant dissociation process as an equilibrium

$$[(C_6H_5)_3SbCH_3^+Br^-] \rightleftharpoons (C_6H_5)_3SbCH_3^+ + Br^-$$

then for an initial concentration C_o added, the actual concentrations are

$$(1-\alpha)C_o \qquad \alpha C_o \qquad \alpha C_o$$

Since the measured conductivity will be determined by the sum of the individual ion conductivities and hence αC_o at a particular ionic strength, i.e. $X \propto \alpha C_o$. The initial rate of change of X may be regarded as occurring in a solution where the concentration C is the only variable (i.e. α and ionic strength constant) so that

$$-Q\frac{dX}{dt} = \frac{-dC}{dt}$$

where Q is simply the ratio of the initial concentration C_o to the initial conductivity X in each case. Thus we can convert $R_c = -dX/dt$ into the initial rate $R_i = -dC/dt$ in each run:

$10^3 C_o$ (mol dm^{-3})	5·987	3·085	1·462	0·7803
$10^4 X$ (ohm^{-1})	36·25	22·46	12·16	7·041
Q (mol dm^{-3} ohm)	1·652	1·374	1·202	1·108
$10^9 R_i$ (mol dm^{-3} s^{-1})	2·637	1·094	0·3464	0·1213

For a bimolecular reaction represented as

$$(C_6H_5)_3SbCH_3^+ + Br^- \rightarrow \text{products}$$

the transition state (activated complex) will have zero charge and its activity coefficient may be taken as unity. According to the transition state theory for reactants A and B having charges Z_A and Z_B respectively, the rate constant for the bimolecular reaction between the two will be given according to the Bronsted–Bjerrum equation in the low ionic strength (I) range

$$\log {}_2k = \log {}_2k_o + 2Z_AZ_BAI^{1/2}$$

where A is a constant for a particular solvent at a defined temperature, which appears in the Deybe–Huckel expression for the activity coefficient (γ) of an ion in solution of ionic strength I,

$$-\log \gamma = AZ^2I^{1/2}$$

In the present case with charges of $+1$ and -1 the expected equation will be

$$\log {}_2k = \log {}_2k_o - 2AI^{1/2} \qquad \text{(i)}$$

where ${}_2k_o$ is the limiting value of ${}_2k$ for $I \rightarrow 0$. The variation of such a rate constant with I is termed the *primary kinetic salt effect*.

In the present case $_2k$ is defined by the rate law

$$R_i = {}_2k[(C_6H_5)_3SbCH_3^+][Br^-] = {}_2k\alpha^2C_o^2$$

while I is determined simply by the extent of dissociation and C_o as

$$I = \tfrac{1}{2}\sum C_iZ^2 = \alpha C_o$$

Hence equation (i) becomes

$$\log\left(\frac{R_i}{\alpha^2C_o^2}\right) = \log {}_2k_o - 2A(\alpha C_o)^{1/2}$$

Therefore a plot of log $(R_i/\alpha^2C_o^2)$ versus $(\alpha C_o)^{1/2}$ should be linear with ordinate intercept of log $_2k_o$. The data for the plot are as follows:

$10^4R_i/\alpha^2C_o^2$ (dm^3 mol^{-1} s^{-1})	1·836	2·116	2·404	2·620
log $(R_i/\alpha^2C_o^2)$	−3·7361	−3·6744	−3·6191	−3·5817
$(\alpha C_o)^{1/2}$ (mol dm^{-3})$^{1/2}$	0·0616	0·0477	0·0347	0·0261

This plot is linear as required and the ordinate intercept is log $({}_2k_o/\text{dm}^3\ \text{mol}^{-1}\ \text{s}^{-1}) = -3{\cdot}47$: hence $_2k_o = 3{\cdot}38 \times 10^{-4}$ dm^3 mol^{-1} s^{-1}.

Example 31

Primary kinetic salt effect (high ionic strength range), third order reaction, Guggenheim formula (activity coefficients) and ion interaction parameters.

The oxidation of ferrous ions by chlorate ions in strongly acid solutions has been shown to obey the third order rate law

$$\frac{-d[Fe^{2+}]}{dt} = {}_3k[Fe^{2+}][H^+][ClO_3^-]$$

Sodium perchlorate ($NaClO_4^-$) can be used to vary the ionic strength (I) of the solution without inducing any complexation of ions and perchloric acid ($HClO_4$) can be used to vary $[H^+]$. The variations of $_3k$ were found at 298 K (where m is molality of $HClO_4$, and $HClO_4$ and $NaClO_4$ may be considered to make the only significant contributions to I):

Experiment number	1	2	3	4	5	6	7	8
$_3k$ (dm^6 mol^{-2} s^{-1})	16·3	19·5	24·6	30·9	13·2	16·5	22·3	36·3
I (mol kg^{-1})	1·80	1·80	1·80	1·80	0·45	1·45	2·20	3·27
m (mol kg^{-1})	0·11	0·50	1·00	1·50	0·40	0·40	0·40	0·40

Show that these results are consistent with a rate-determining step with reactant stoichiometry $Fe^{2+} + H^+ + ClO_3^-$, to which transition state theory can be applied using the Guggenheim formula for the activity coefficient of an ion i expressed as

$$\log \gamma_i = -\frac{AZ_i^2I^{1/2}}{1+I^{1/2}} + \sum_j B(i,j)m_j \qquad (A = 0{\cdot}5 \text{ here})$$

The summation is taken over all other species, j, in solution: m_j is the molality of the ion j and $B(i, j)$ is a specific ion interaction parameter, equal to zero when i is an ion of the same sign of charge as j. Z_i is the charge of the ion i.

Evaluate $\{B(H^+, ClO_3^-) - B(Na^+, ClO_3^-)\}$ and the limiting value of $_3k$ for zero ionic strength.

Source: Ang, K. P., Creek, G. A., and Kwik, W. L., (1972) *Journal of the Chemical Society, Dalton Transactions,* p. 2560. (Singapore)

Solution

For a termolecular reaction forming the transition state, represented

$$Fe^{2+} + H^+ + ClO_3^- \rightarrow \ddagger^{2+}$$

the transition state theory formulation of the rate constant is

$$_3k = \frac{k^\ddagger K^\ddagger \gamma_{Fe^{2+}} \gamma_{H^+} \gamma_{ClO_3^-}}{\gamma_\ddagger}$$

where $k^\ddagger$ and $K^\ddagger$ are constants and $\gamma^\ddagger$ is the activity coefficient of the transition state. Hence, on substituting the Guggenheim formula for the activity coefficients, we obtain

$$\log {_3k} = \log {_3k_o} - \frac{AI^{1/2}}{1 + I^{1/2}}(2^2 + 1^2 + 1^2 - 2^2) + \sum_j B(i, j)m_j \qquad \text{(i)}$$

where $_3k_o$ is the rate constant at zero ionic strength.

The data given divide into two sets:

(*a*) Variation of m at constant I (experiments 1 to 4).

(*b*) Variation of I at constant m (experiments 5 to 8).

In explicit form, equation (i) becomes (ignoring the small concentrations of Fe^{2+} and ClO_3^-)

$$\log {_3k} = \left(\log {_3k_o} - \frac{2AI^{1/2}}{1 + I^{1/2}}\right) + \{B(Fe^{2+}, ClO_4^-) + B(H^+, ClO_4^-) \qquad \text{(ii)}$$
$$- B(\ddagger, ClO_4^-)\}m_{ClO_4^-} + B(Na^+, ClO_3^-)m_{Na^+} + B(H^+, ClO_3^-)m$$

Also we have the relationship demanded by the electroneutrality of the solution

$$m_{ClO_4^-} = m_{Na^+} + m \qquad \text{(iii)}$$

For set (*a*) of the experiments we have constant I and hence $m_{ClO_4^-}$ and on grouping all of the constant terms in equation (ii) with substitution of equation (iii) we obtain

$$\log {_3k} = \text{constant} + \{B(H^+, ClO_3^-) - B(Na^+, ClO_3^-)\}m$$

Thus for set (*a*) a plot of log $_3k$ versus m should be linear with gradient equal to the required parameter $\{B(H^+, ClO_3^-) - B(Na^+, ClO_3^-)\}$ and ordinate intercept as below

$$\text{intercept} = \log {}_3k_o - \frac{I^{1/2}}{1+I^{1/2}} + \{B(Fe^{2+}, ClO_4^-) + B(H^+, ClO_4^-) - B(\ddagger, ClO_4^-) + B(Na^+, ClO_3^-)\} m_{ClO_4^-} \quad \text{(iv)}$$

taking $A = 0{\cdot}5$ in equation (ii) as given. The data for the plot are:

log ($_3k$)	1·212	1·2900	1·3909	1·4900
m (mol kg^{-1})	0·11	0·50	1·00	1·50

This plot is linear with gradient of 0·199 kg mol^{-1} and intercept of 1·191. Thus we derive $\{B(H^+, ClO_3^-) - B(Na^+, ClO_3^-)\} = 0{\cdot}199$ kg mol^{-1}.

For set (*b*) of the data with m constant but I and hence $m_{ClO_4^-}$ varying, we shall have the recast form of equation (ii)

$$\log {}_3k + \frac{I^{1/2}}{1+I^{1/2}} = \text{constant} + \{B(Fe^{+2}, ClO_4^-) + B(H^+, ClO_4^-) - B(\ddagger, ClO_4^-) + B(Na^+, ClO_3^-)\} m_{ClO_4^-} \quad \text{(v)}$$

Thus we expect a linear plot of log $_3k + I^{1/2}/(1+I^{1/2})$ versus $m_{ClO_4^-}$ and the data for this plot are as follows:

log ($_3k$)$+I^{1/2}/(1+I^{1/2})$	1·522	1·764	1·946	2·204
$m_{ClO_4^-}$ (mol kg^{-1})	0·45	1·45	2·20	3·27

This plot is linear with gradient of 0·242 kg mol^{-1} and it is to be noted that this combination of B terms appears in equation (iv) as part of the intercept of the plot of set (*a*) data, evaluated as 1·191. Hence, since the set (*a*) data all have $I = 1{\cdot}80$ mol kg^{-1} so that $I^{1/2}/(1+I^{1/2}) = 0{\cdot}573$, and $m_{ClO_4^-} = 1{\cdot}80$ kg mol^{-1}, equation (iv) becomes

$$1{\cdot}191 = \log {}_3k_o - 0{\cdot}573 + (0{\cdot}242 \times 1{\cdot}80)$$

and log $_3k_o = 1{\cdot}336$ so that $_3k_o = 21{\cdot}7$ dm^6 mol^{-2} s^{-1}, representing the value of $_3k$ extrapolated to zero ionic strength.

The intercept of the plot of the set (*b*) data is 1·412 and this is to be equated to the constant in equation (v), i.e.

$$1{\cdot}412 = \log {}_3k_o + \{B(H^+, ClO_3^-) - B(Na^+, ClO_3^-)\} m$$

According to the difference of the B terms obtained above, the second term on the right-hand side is equal to $0{\cdot}199m = 0{\cdot}199 \times 0{\cdot}40 = 8{\cdot}0 \times 10^{-2}$. Thus on rearrangement we obtain the equation

$$\log {}_3k_o = 1{\cdot}412 - 0{\cdot}08 = 1{\cdot}332$$

which is in acceptable agreement with the result derived from set (*a*.)

It should be noted that in the above treatment, where the rate constant ${}_3k$ is defined from concentrations, we have assumed a direct proportionality between molality and concentration for the species Fe^{2+}, ClO_3^- and H^+, which will not introduce significant error in aqueous solutions where the molality of the solvent is 55·5 mol kg^{-1} and the molalities of the reactants do not exceed 1·5 mol kg^{-1}.

It can also be noted that for solutions in the range intermediate between the ionic strengths where the Debye–Huckel equation can be applied (concentrations of the order of 10^{-3} mol dm^{-3} and below (in total)) and those where the full Guggenheim formula must be used (generally involving total concentrations of the order of 0·1 mol dm^{-3} and above), it is usually possible to apply the intermediate form

$$\log \gamma_i = -\frac{AZ_i^2 I^{1/2}}{1+I^{1/2}}$$

without introducing significant error.

SECTION SEVEN

HOMOGENEOUS CATALYSIS

Example 32

Acid/base catalysis, specific acid catalysis, spontaneous reaction, scavenger, inhibition.

The kinetics of dehydration of glyoxylic acid (HA) have been studied in aqueous solution, using scavenger molecules to destroy the aldehyde product and thus to inhibit completely the reverse hydration to reform HA. The results were fitted to a rate law of the form

$$-\frac{d[\mathrm{HA}]_\mathrm{T}}{dt} = k_{\mathrm{obs}}[\mathrm{HA}]_\mathrm{T}$$

where $[\mathrm{HA}]_\mathrm{T}$ represents the total glyoxylic acid concentration present as HA or the anion A^-: the acid dissociation equilibrium $\mathrm{HA} \rightleftharpoons \mathrm{H}^+ + \mathrm{A}^-$ is maintained under all conditions here. The pH of the solution was adjusted with strong acid additions and at constant ionic strength at 298 K the following results were obtained:

$10^3 k_{\mathrm{obs}}$ (s^{-1})	49·0	32·5	27·1	24·6	22·6	18·5	13·1	8·75	5·88	5·54
pH	0·5	1·0	1·5	2·0	2·5	3·0	3·5	4·0	5·0	6·0

Interpret these results on the basis of spontaneous and specific acid-catalysed dehydrations of both HA and A^- operating in the absence of specific base catalysis for pH less than 6. Evaluate the distinguishable rate constants given that pK = 3·30 for glyoxylic acid, assuming that all activity coefficients are unity.

Source: Sorensen, P. E., Bruhn, K. and Lindelov, F. (1974) *Acta Chemica Scandanavica*, **A28**, p. 162. (Denmark)

Solution

The detailed rate law which takes account of spontaneous and specific acid-catalysed dehydrations of HA and A^- will be:

$$\text{rate} = (k_\mathrm{o}^{\mathrm{HA}} + k_\mathrm{H}^{\mathrm{HA}}[\mathrm{H}^+])[\mathrm{HA}] + (k_\mathrm{o}^{\mathrm{A}} + k_\mathrm{H}^{\mathrm{A}}[\mathrm{H}^+])[\mathrm{A}^-]$$

where the k are rate constants such that the subscripts o correspond to the spontaneous reactions and the subscripts H correspond to the specific acid-catalysed reactions, with the superscripts indicating the actual reactant.

We define $K=[H^+][A^-]/[HA]$ as the concentration equilibrium constant and we must now obtain expressions for [HA] and $[A^-]$ in terms of $[H^+]$ and $[HA]_T$.

$$[HA]_T = [HA]+[A^-] = [HA]+K\frac{[HA]}{[H^+]}$$

and

$$[HA] = \frac{[HA]_T[H^+]}{[H^+]+K} \qquad \text{(i)}$$

Also

$$[A^-] = K\frac{[HA]}{[H^+]}$$

$$= K\frac{[HA]_T}{[H^+]+K} \qquad \text{(ii)}$$

One simplification which we can make in the rate law before substituting equations (i) and (ii) comes from noting that the last term $k_H^A[H^+][A^-]$ can be expressed as $k_H^A K[HA]$. Thus the specific acid catalysis for A^- produces a term in the rate law which is indistinguishable kinetically from that arising from the spontaneous dehydration of HA, viz. $k_o^{HA}[HA]$. Thus if we use $k_o=(k_o^{HA}+k_H^A K)$, then the rate law will become

$$\text{rate} = \left\{\frac{k_o+k_H^{HA}[H^+]}{1+\dfrac{K}{[H^+]}}+\frac{k_o^A}{1+\dfrac{[H^+]}{K}}\right\}[HA]_T = k_{obs}[HA]_T$$

on substitution of equations (i) and (ii). Thus k_{obs} is composed of three terms:

$$k_{obs} = \frac{k_o^A}{1+\dfrac{[H^+]}{K}}+\frac{k_o}{1+\dfrac{K}{[H^+]}}+\frac{k_H^{HA}[H^+]}{1+\dfrac{K}{[H^+]}} \qquad \text{(iii)}$$

arranged in likely order of decreasing magnitude at higher pH.

The given data show that k_{obs} is almost constant between pH 5 and 6 and since pK$=3{\cdot}30$, $K=10^{-3\cdot30}$ mol dm^{-3} (i.e. $\ll 1$), this means that at pH$=6$, the first term in equation (iii) can be equated to k_{obs} as follows:

$$\frac{k_o^A}{1+\dfrac{10^{-6}}{10^{-3\cdot30}}} \simeq k_o^A = 5{\cdot}54\times10^{-3}\ \text{s}^{-1}$$

Now this term will evidently decrease in significance as pH decreases, e.g. at pH = 2, its denominator is $1+10^{1\cdot3}=20\cdot96$ and the contribution of the first term of equation (iii) is only $2\cdot6\times10^{-4}$ s^{-1} to a value given of $2\cdot46\times10^{-2}$ s^{-1} for k_{obs}, which can be regarded as effectively negligible.

Therefore, for the data below pH = 2, we may approximate accurately enough by equating k_{obs} to the last two terms of equation (iii) and therefore we expect a plot of $k_{obs}\,(1+K/[H^+])$ versus $[H^+]$ to be linear with ordinate intercept equal to k_o and gradient equal to k_H^{HA}. The data for the plot are as follows:

k_{obs} (s^{-1})	0·0490	0·0325	0·0271	0·0246
$[H^+]$ (mol dm^{-3})	0·316	0·100	0·0316	0·010
$k_{obs}(1+K/[H^+])$ (s^{-1})	0·0491	0·0327	0·0275	0·0258

The plot is strongly linear and we obtain:

$$\text{intercept} = k_o = 0\cdot025\ \text{s}^{-1}$$

$$\text{gradient} = k_H^{HA} = 0\cdot075\ \text{dm}^3\ \text{mol}^{-1}\ \text{s}^{-1}.$$

Finally we should check that we can predict at least one of the values of k_{obs} for pH between 2 and 6, using the above rate constant values, say $k_{obs}=8\cdot75\times10^{-3}$ s^{-1} at pH = 4. For $[H^+]=10^{-4}$ mol dm^{-3} and $K=5\cdot0\times10^{-4}$ mol dm^{-3}, equation (iii) becomes

$$k_{obs}=\frac{5\cdot54\times10^{-3}}{1+0\cdot2}+\frac{0\cdot025}{1+5\cdot0}+\frac{7\cdot5\times10^{-6}}{1+5\cdot0}$$

$$=4\cdot62\times10^{-3}+4\cdot17\times10^{-3}+1\cdot25\times10^{-6}$$

$$=8\cdot79\times10^{-3}\ \text{s}^{-1}$$

in close agreement with the tabulated result.

Example 33

Acid/base catalysis, general acid and general base catalysis, specific acid and specific base catalysis.

The rate of iodination of acetone is controlled by acid/base catalysis, operating on the rate-determining enolisation step. The experimental rate law can be expressed by the equation

$$-\frac{d[I_2]}{dt}=k_{obs}\,[\text{acetone}] \qquad (\text{independent of } [I_2])$$

The rate of consumption of iodine has been followed using the tri-iodide (I_3^-) ion absorption at a wavelength of 353 nm in $H_2PO_4^-/HPO_4^{2-}$ buffered solutions containing a trace of iodide ion. It was found that plots of k_{obs}

versus $[HPO_4^{2-}]$ were linear for a given buffer ratio, $r = [HPO_4^{2-}]/[H_2PO_4^-]$, with slopes ($S$) varying as a function of r as follows ($[HPO_4^{2-}] \geqslant 0{\cdot}01$ mol dm^{-3}):

$10^4 S$ (dm^3 mol^{-1} min^{-1})	10·4	5·67	3·94	3·02	1·64
r	1·50	2·75	3·96	5·17	9·51

Show that specific acid and specific base catalysis are insignificant under these conditions and evaluate the rate constant(s) for general acid and/or general base catalysis.

In other experiments, it has been found that the rate constant for specific acid catalysis of this reaction is $3{\cdot}3 \times 10^{-5}$ dm^3 mol^{-1} s^{-1} for the same physical conditions as above. On the basis that pK for the second hydrogen ionisation constant of phosphoric acid (H_3PO_4) is 6·90, confirm that specific acid catalysis is of negligible significance in the buffered solutions above.

Source: Spaulding, J., Stein, J. E. and Meany, J. E. (1977) *Journal of Physical Chemistry*, **81**, p. 1359. (U.S.A.)

Solution

The general expression for the observed rate constant in acid/base catalysis takes the form

$$k_{obs} = k_o + k_H[H^+] + k_{OH}[OH^-] + k_A[A] + k_B[B]$$

where k_O is the rate constant for the spontaneous process, k_H and k_{OH} are the rate constants for specific acid and specific base catalysis respectively and k_A and k_B are the rate constants for general acid and general base catalysis respectively. In the present case A is identified with $H_2PO_4^-$ and B with the conjugate base HPO_4^{2-}, so that $r = [A]/[B]$. It follows that

$$k_{obs} = (k_o + k_H[H^+] + k_{OH}[OH^-]) + [A]\left(k_A + \frac{k_B}{r}\right)$$

Under circumstances where the specific catalysis terms are expected to be insignificant, a linear plot of k_{obs} versus [A] for a defined r, as observed, is expected and the slope, S, will be equal to $(k_A + k_B/r)$. Thus a further plot of S versus r^{-1} should be linear with intercept k_A and slope k_B. The data for the plot are as follows:

$10^4 S$ (dm^3 mol^{-1} min^{-1})	10·4	5·67	3·94	3·02	1·64
r^{-1}	0·667	0·364	0·253	0·193	0·105

The plot turns out to be linear and passes through the origin. Hence the intercept $k_A = 0$, while the slope $k_B = 1{\cdot}56 \times 10^{-3}$ dm^3 mol^{-1} min^{-1}: thus the reaction is subject only to general base catalysis by HPO_4^{2-} and $H_2PO_4^-$ does not catalyse the reaction as far as can be seen within the precision of the present data.

Since pK for the second hydrogen ionisation of H_3PO_4 is 6·90, we shall have $K = 1{\cdot}26\times10^{-7}$ mol dm^{-3} $=[H^+][HPO_4^{2-}]/[H_2PO_4^-]=[H^+]r$. Hence with r in the range 1·50 to 9·51, $[H^+]$ will be in the range $8{\cdot}4\times10^{-8}$ mol dm^{-3} to $1{\cdot}32\times10^{-8}$ mol dm^{-3}. With $k_H=3{\cdot}3\times10^{-5}$ dm^3 mol^{-1} s^{-1}, the contribution of the specific acid catalysis term $k_H[H^+]$ is less than $2{\cdot}8\times10^{-12}$ s^{-1} $=1{\cdot}7\times10^{-10}$ min^{-1}. For $[HPO_4^{2-}]\geqslant0{\cdot}01$ mol dm^{-3}, the general base catalysis term $k_B[B]$ will be greater than $1{\cdot}56\times10^{-3}\times0{\cdot}01=1{\cdot}56\times10^{-5}$ min^{-1}, which will make the contribution from specific acid catalysis around five orders of magnitude less and therefore of negligible significance.

Example 34

Enzyme-catalysed reaction, Michaelis–Menten mechanism, Lineweaver–Burk plot, competitive/uncompetitive/noncompetitive inhibition, Michaelis constant, initial rates method.

Alcohol dehydrogenase catalyses the oxidation of ethanol to acetaldehyde in aqueous solutions. Initial rates (R_i) of reaction at 298 K for ethanol (in the absence of acetaldehyde) in the presence of a small, constant enzyme concentration in solution of pH = 7·9 were as follows:

$[C_2H_5OH]$ (mol dm^{-3})	0·01	0·02	0·05	0·10
10^3R_i (mol dm^{-3} s^{-1})	1·58	2·63	4·36	5·59

Calculate the maximum initial rate and Michaelis constant values for these conditions.

When $1{\cdot}0\times10^{-2}$ mol dm^{-3} of hydroxylamine was present, the R_i measured were as follows (for the same $[C_2H_5OH]$ in order as above):

10^3R_i (mol dm^{-3} s^{-1})	1·42	2·40	4·10	5·38

When $4{\cdot}0\times10^{-4}$ mol dm^{-3} of p-chloromercuribenzoate was present, the R_i measured were as follows (for the same $[C_2H_5OH]$ in order as above):

10^3R_i (mol dm^{-3} s^{-1})	0·89	1·48	2·46	3·16

Determine the types of inhibition involved in both cases and the values of the equilibrium constants for the inhibitor complexes formed.

Source: Sindelar, L., Bacik, Z. and Sarhan, J. (1977) *Collection of Czechoslovak Chemical Communications,* **42**, p. 3539. (Czechoslovakia)

Solution

The Michaelis–Menten mechanism for the reaction of an enzyme E and a substrate S takes the form

$$E + S \rightleftarrows ES \qquad ES \rightarrow E + \text{products}$$

where ES is regarded as a weakly-bound complex. Analysis of the mechanism yields

$$R_i = \frac{V_{max}[S]}{K_m + [S]}$$

where V_{max} is the maximum initial rate for the enzyme concentration present and K_m is the Michaelis constant. Inversion of both sides yields

$$R_i^{-1} = (V_{max})^{-1} + \frac{K_m}{V_{max}}[S]^{-1}$$

This predicts the linear form of the Lineweaver–Burk plot of reciprocal rate against reciprocal substrate concentration, with intercept on the ordinate of $(V_{max})^{-1}$ and gradient K_m/V_{max}. Accordingly the data to be plotted for the uninhibited reaction are as follows:

R_i^{-1} (dm^3 mol^{-1} s)	633	380	229	179
$[C_2H_5OH]^{-1}$ (dm^3 mol^{-1})	100	50	20	10

The plot is linear with gradient of 5·06 s and intercept of 129 dm^3 mol^{-1} s. Hence $V_{max} = 7{\cdot}8 \times 10^{-3}$ mol dm^{-3} s^{-1} and $K_m = 3{\cdot}9 \times 10^{-2}$ mol dm^{-3}.

There are three mechanisms of inhibition of enzyme catalysis on the basis of the Michaelis–Menten mechanism, distinguished on the basis of the species with which the inhibitor (I) complexes.

(i) Competitive Inhibition—complexation of I with E only, with an equilibrium constant defined as $K_I = [E][I]/[EI]$. Stationary state analysis of the Michaelis–Menten mechanism with this additional equilibrium leads to the equation

$$R_i^{-1} = (V_{max})^{-1} + \frac{K_m}{V_{max}}\left(1 + \frac{[I]}{K_I}\right)[S]^{-1} \qquad \text{(i)}$$

This indicates a Lineweaver–Burk plot of the same intercept but increased gradient compared to the uninhibited reaction.

(ii) Uncompetitive Inhibition—complexation of I with ES only, with an equilibrium constant defined as $k_I = [ES][I]/[ESI]$. Stationary state analysis of this mechanism yields the equation

$$R_i^{-1} = (V_{max})^{-1}\left(1 + \frac{[I]}{K_I}\right) + \frac{K_m}{V_{max}}[S]^{-1} \qquad \text{(ii)}$$

This indicates a Lineweaver–Burk plot of increased intercept but unchanged gradient compared to the uninhibited reaction.

(iii) Noncompetitive Inhibition—complexation of I with both E and ES, with the usual circumstance that the same equilibrium constant (as defined in (i) and (ii) above) value applies to both equilibria involving I, understandable if I does not bind at the same enzyme site as S. Stationary state analysis of the mechanism here yields the equation

$$R_i^{-1} = (V_{max})^{-1}\left(1 + \frac{[I]}{K_I}\right) + \frac{K_m}{V_{max}}\left(1 + \frac{[I]}{K_I}\right)[S]^{-1} \qquad \text{(iii)}$$

This indicates a Lineweaver–Burk plot with both intercept and gradient increased by the same factor compared with the uninhibited reaction.

Accordingly we now proceed to plot the data for the two cases of inhibition concerned here in Lineweaver–Burk plots for which the data are:

$[C_2H_5OH]^{-1}$ ($dm^3\ mol^{-1}$)	100	50	20	10
(*a*) R_i^{-1} ($dm^3\ mol^{-1}\ s$)	704	417	244	186
(*b*) R_i^{-1} ($dm^3\ mol^{-1}\ s$)	1124	676	407	316

(where the inhibitor (I) in (*a*) is hydroxylamine and in (*b*) is p-chloromercuribenzoate).

Both plots are linear. The plot for I = hydroxylamine has the same intercept as the uninhibited plot but a gradient increased by a factor of 1·14 for $[I] = 1{\cdot}0 \times 10^{-2}$ mol dm^{-3}. Hence this is competititive inhibition and $K_I = 1{\cdot}0 \times 10^{-2}/0{\cdot}14 = 7{\cdot}1 \times 10^{-2}$ mol dm^{-3} on the basis of equation (i).

On the other hand, the plot for I = p-chloromercuribenzoate has both gradient and intercept increased by a common factor of 1·77 compared to the unihibited plot. On the basis of equation (iii), this is noncompetitive inhibition. With $[I] = 4{\cdot}0 \times 10^{-4}$ mol dm^{-3}, and $(1 + [I]/K_I) = 1{\cdot}77$, we have $K_I = 4{\cdot}0 \times 10^{-4}/0{\cdot}77 = 5{\cdot}2 \times 10^{-4}$ mol dm^{-3}.

SECTION EIGHT

HETEROGENEOUS CATALYSIS

Example 35

Langmuir adsorption isotherm, physical adsorption, chemisorption, Langmuir–Hinshelwood mechanism, Arrhenius activation energy (apparent), microcalorimetry, isolation method (reaction orders), pseudo-order reaction.

The heterogeneous hydrogen–oxygen reaction has been studied using a microcalorimetric technique, where the difference in electrical power (ΔW) required to maintain the platinum wire calorimeter/catalyst at a given temperature, in the presence and absence of the catalytic reaction, is a direct measure of the rate. Two different surfaces, "oxidised" and "reduced", were established by appropriate pre-treatment.

On the "reduced" surface, ΔW was directly proportional to the partial pressure of oxygen, P_{O_2}, for constant partial pressure of hydrogen, P_{H_2}, and was also proportional to $P_{H_2}^{-1/2}$ for constant P_{O_2}. The apparent activation energy of the overall rate constant was 49 kJ mol^{-1}.

On the "oxidised" surface, ΔW was independent of P_{O_2} at constant P_{H_2}, while at constant P_{O_2} the variation of ΔW with P_{H_2} at 369 K was observed to be a direct proportionality at the lowest values of P_{H_2} with a gradual transition to independence of P_{H_2} at the highest partial pressures. The apparent activation energies of the two pseudo-rate constants in these two limiting regions were 64 kJ mol^{-1} and 83 kJ mol^{-1} respectively.

Devise Langmuir–Hinshelwood mechanisms for the two catalyst surfaces consistent with the above observations and determine the nature of the adsorption of hydrogen on each.

Source: Gentry, S. J., Firth, J. G. and Jones, A. (1974) *Journal of the Chemical Society, Faraday Transactions I*, **70**, p. 600 (U.K.)

Solution

Since a constant amount of heat will be released to the microcalorimeter by each hydrogen molecule oxidised, the direct proportionality of ΔW to $-d[H_2]/dt$ is obvious.

"*Reduced*" *surface* The observations indicate a rate law of the form (each partial order isolated)

$$\frac{-d[H_2]}{dt} = \frac{k_o[O_2]}{[H_2]^{1/2}}$$

where k_O is the effective rate constant. The half power in $[H_2]$ immediately suggests that hydrogen is chemisorbed in the atomic form.

The Langmuir adsorption isotherm approach equates the rates of adsorption and desorption for the $H_2(g) \rightleftharpoons 2H_{ads}$ system, yielding the equation

$$k_1 P_{H_2}(1-\theta_H)^2 = k_2\theta_H^2$$

where k_1 and k_2 are constants and θ_H is the fraction of surface sites occupied by H atoms. On rearrangement we obtain

$$\frac{\theta_H}{1-\theta_H} = \left(\frac{k_1}{k_2}\right)^{1/2} P_{H_2}^{1/2}$$

and

$$\theta_H = \frac{(k_1/k_2)^{1/2}\, P_{H_2}^{1/2}}{1+(k_1/k_2)^{1/2}\, P_{H_2}^{1/2}}$$

If the rate-determining step of the overall reaction were either adsorption of hydrogen or surface reaction between adsorbed H and O_2 adsorbed on separate sites, then

$$\Delta W \propto \theta_H \propto \frac{P_{H_2}^{1/2}}{\text{constant} + P_{H_2}^{1/2}}$$

which is not the observed behaviour. The other possibility is that H and O_2 compete for the same surface sites. The Langmuir adsorption isotherm equations would then be

$$k_1 P_{H_2}(1-\theta_H-\theta_{O_2})^2 = k_2\theta_H^2 \qquad \text{(i)}$$

$$k_3 P_{O_2}(1-\theta_H-\theta_{O_2}) = k_4\theta_{O_2} \qquad \text{(ii)}$$

where the k values are constant and θ_{O_2} is the fraction of surface sites occupied by oxygen molecules, assumed not to be dissociatively adsorbed in the first instance and to occupy a single site when adsorbed. Taking equations (i) and (ii) in the form of equating the ratio of the square root of the left hand side of (i) and the left-hand side of (ii) to the same ratio composed from the right hand sides, we obtain

$$\frac{(k_1 P_{H_2})^{1/2}}{k_3 P_{O_2}} = \frac{k_2^{1/2}\theta_H}{k_4\theta_{O_2}} \qquad \text{(iii)}$$

On substituting for θ_H in equation (ii) using equation (iii) we obtain

$$k_3 P_{O_2}\left(1 - \frac{k_4 k_1^{1/2} P_{H_2}^{1/2}}{k_3 k_2^{1/2} P_{O_2}}\theta_{O_2} - \theta_{O_2}\right) = k_4\theta_{O_2}$$

and hence on rearrangement

$$\theta_{O_2} = \frac{k_{O_2} P_{O_2}}{1 + k_H P_{H_2}^{1/2} + k_{O_2} P_{O_2}}$$

where the constants are defined as $k_H = (k_1/k_2)^{1/2}$ and $k_{O_2} = k_3/k_4$. Then from equation (iii) we derive

$$\theta_H = \frac{k_H P_{H_2}^{1/2}}{1 + k_H P_{H_2}^{1/2} + k_{O_2} P_{O_2}}$$

Now if the surface reaction between adsorbed H and O_2, with effective rate constant k_s, is rate-determining for the overall reaction, we shall have

$$\Delta W = k_s \theta_H \theta_{O_2} \propto \frac{P_{O_2} P_{H_2}^{1/2}}{(1 + k_H P_{H_2}^{1/2} + k_{O_2} P_{O_2})^2}$$

Now if it is the case that H atoms are very strongly adsorbed then we can expect $k_H P_{H_2}^{1/2}$ to be very much greater than $1 + k_{O_2} P_{O_2}$, so that the effective relationship becomes

$$\Delta W = \frac{k_o P_{O_2}}{P_{H_2}^{1/2}}$$

which is the observed rate law.

The apparent activation energy of the effective rate constant $k_O = k_s k_{O_2}/k_H^{1/2}$ will be $E_a = E_s - q_{O_2} + \frac{1}{2}q_{H_2}$, where E_s is the true activation energy of the surface reaction and q is the heat released on adsorption of the subscripted species. No deductions can be made on the magnitude of each term from the information given, beyond $E_a = 49\ \text{kJ mol}^{-1}$.

"Oxidized" surface The zero order behaviour with respect to O_2 must be considered as reflecting strong adsorption (and therefore chemisorption) and complete coverage of available surface sites by O_2. Since O_2 is a small molecule, a geometric factor cannot operate to produce ill-fitting (as for

bulky molecules) and consequent unoccupied sites (on a statistical basis) for hydrogen adsorption. On the other hand, hydrogen shows a transition from first order kinetic behaviour at low P_{H_2} to zero order behaviour at high P_{H_2}, interpreted on the basis of the Langmuir adsorption isotherm as reflecting transition from low surface coverage to high surface coverage as P_{H_2} increases. It is then clear that in this case the two species do not compete for the same sites, and molecular hydrogen on the surface is an effective reactant. This suggests that H_2 is only physically adsorbed, since chemisorption might be expected to involve adsorbed H atoms as in the previous case. In this event, the Langmuir isotherm interpretation of the apparent activation energy (E_a) is that at low H_2 surface coverage

$$E_a = E_T - q_{H_2}$$

where E_T is the true activation energy of the surface reaction between adsorbed H_2 and adsorbed oxygen and q_{H_2} is the heat released by adsorption of the weakly-adsorbed H_2. Under the zero order conditions at high P_{H_2}, $E_a = E_T$: hence the difference between the two limiting values of E_a quoted ($83-64=19$ kJ mol^{-1}) is equal to q_{H_2}. The low value of 19 kJ mol^{-1} again indicates physical adsorption of H_2, since chemisorption would be expected to involve a much larger heat release (of the order of 100 kJ mol^{-1} usually).

Example 36

Unimolecular heterogeneous reaction, Langmuir adsorption isotherm, enthalpy of adsorption, Arrhenius activation energy (apparent), initial rates method, reaction order (apparent).

The initial rate (R_i) of cis to trans isomerisation of 2-butene on a silica-alumina catalyst has been measured as a function of cis-2-butene pressure (P). An apparent reaction order, n, has been determined on the basis that $R_i \propto P^n$ for a particular value of P at various temperatures (T), with the values of n being as tabulated below:

T (K)	P (kPa)			
	1·30	2·00	2·66	3·99
338	0·64	0·54	0·47	0·37
348	0·79	0·71	0·65	0·55
358	0·88	0·83	0·78	0·70

By extrapolation, the limiting high pressure (zero order) values of R_i were estimated to be as follows:

$10^8 R_i$ (mol s^{-1} m^{-2})	0·17	0·42	1·0
T (K)	338	348	358

Use these data to evaluate on the basis of the Langmuir adsorption isotherm:

(*a*) ΔH for adsorption of cis-2-butene on the surface,

(*b*) The true activation energy for the unimolecular surface reaction,

(*c*) The limiting, low pressure, apparent activation energy.

Source: Ballivet, D., Barthomeuf, D. and Trambouze, Y. (1974) *Journal of Catalysis,* **34**, p. 423. (France)

Solution

(*a*) The Langmuir adsorption isotherm view of a unimolecular surface reaction predicts $R_i \propto \theta$, the fraction of surface sites covered by reactant molecules, with $\theta = k_1P/(k_2+k_1P)$, where k_1 and k_2 are the effective rate constants for adsorption and desorption respectively. Defining $b = k_1/k_2$ as the effective equilibrium constant, then $b \propto \exp(-\Delta H/RT)$, where ΔH is the enthalpy change for adsorption of the reactant, cis-2-butene in this case. Upon inserting b into the above expression for θ, we obtain

$$R_i \propto \frac{P}{1+bP} = f(P)P^n$$

where $f(P)$ is the function of P required for dimensional balance. For infinitesimal changes in P, $f(P)$ and n can be considered as constants. Thus taking logarithms of the above equation

$$\ln P - \ln(1+bP) = \ln f(P) + n \ln P$$

$$(1-n)\ln P = \ln f(P) + \ln(1+bP)$$

Upon differentiation with respect to P we obtain

$$(1-n)\frac{d\ln P}{dP} = \frac{d\ln(1+bP)}{dP}$$

$$\frac{1-n}{P} = \frac{b}{1+bP}$$

i.e.

$$b = \frac{1-n}{nP}$$

Thus values of $(1-n)/nP = b$ should be constant for each temperature, T, as shown in the table below:

$T = 338$ K	n	0·64	0·54	0·47	0·37
	P (kPa)	1·30	2·00	2·66	3·99
	b (kP^{-1})	0·43	0·43	0·42	0·43
$T = 348$ K	n	0·79	0·71	0·65	0·55
	b (kPa^{-1})	0·21	0·20	0·20	0·21
$T = 358$ K	n	0·88	0·83	0·78	0·70
	b (kPa^{-1})	0·10	0·10	0·11	0·11

Within the limits of precision imposed by two significant figures, the values of b at each temperature are acceptably constant and the average values are $b=0{\cdot}43$, $0{\cdot}21$ and $0{\cdot}11\ \mathrm{kPa^{-1}}$ at $T=338$ K, 348 K and 358 K respectively. According to the proportionality quoted above, a plot of $\ln b$ versus T^{-1} should be linear with gradient of $-\Delta H/R$. The data for the plot are:

$\ln b$	$-0{\cdot}844$	$-1{\cdot}561$	$-2{\cdot}207$
$10^3\ \mathrm{K}/T$	2·959	2·874	2·793

The plot is closely linear with gradient of $+8{\cdot}2\times10^3\ \mathrm{K}=-\Delta H/R$, so that $\Delta H=-68\ \mathrm{kJ\ mol^{-1}}$.

(*b*) The limiting high pressure values of R_i are obtained with $\theta=1$, so that $R_i=k_s$, the effective rate constant for surface reaction. An Arrhenius plot of $\ln R_i$ versus T^{-1} will be expected to have gradient equal to $-E_T/R$, where E_T is the true activation energy for the surface reaction. The data for the plot are as follows:

$\ln R_i$	$-20{\cdot}193$	$-19{\cdot}288$	$-18{\cdot}421$
$10^3\ \mathrm{K}/T$	2·959	2·874	2·793

This plot is linear with gradient of $-1{\cdot}1\times10^4\ \mathrm{K}=-E_T/R$, so that $E_T=91$ kJ mol^{-1}.

(*c*) In the limiting low-pressure region, we shall have

$$R_i = k_s\theta \simeq k_s bP \qquad (1 \gg bP)$$

and the apparent activation energy E_a will be given by

$$-\frac{E_a}{R}=\frac{d\ln k_s}{d(T^{-1})}+\frac{d\ln b}{d(T^{-1})}=\frac{-E_T}{R}-\frac{\Delta H}{R}$$

i.e.

$$E_a = E_T+\Delta H = 91-68 = 23\ \mathrm{kJ\ mol^{-1}}$$

Example 37

Eley-Rideal mechanism, integrated rate laws (fractional order reactions), isolation method, static constant volume gas reactor.

Carbon monoxide and oxygen gases in 2:1 molar ratio have been reacted on a granular ZnO catalyst in a static constant volume reactor at 533 K and carbon dioxide was the only product. The partial pressure of carbon monoxide (P_{CO}) at time t after the start of reaction was deduced from the corresponding total pressure and plots of $P_{CO}^{-1/2}$ versus t proved to be linear.

When the molar ratio of $CO:O_2$ was increased to 255:20, a linear plot of $P_{O_2}^{1/2}$ versus t was obtained, where P_{O_2} is the partial pressure of oxygen.

Deduce the order of the reaction with respect to each reactant.

Show that the experimental rate law would be predicted by an Eley-Rideal mechanism of heterogeneous catalysis, where an equilibrium is maintained between O_2 gas and a *low* surface coverage of O^- ions, the latter react with CO molecules in the gas phase in the rate-determining step while CO is very strongly adsorbed onto the ZnO surface, but at different sites from O^-.

Source: Choi, J. S. and Kim, B. W. (1972) *Bulletin of the Chemical Society of Japan*, **45**, p. 21. (South Korea)

Solution

Since CO_2 is the only product, the stoichiometric equation is

$$2CO + O_2 \rightarrow 2CO_2$$

The first set of experiments were conducted therefore with the stoichiometric ratio of CO and O_2, so that at all times t, $P_{CO} = 2P_{O_2}$. Let the rate law be expressed as

$$-\frac{1}{2}\frac{dP_{CO}}{dt} = {}_nkP_{CO}^{p}P_{O2}^{q} \propto P_{CO}^{(p+q)}$$

where p and q are the partial orders. After collection of variables to opposite sides we obtain the integral equation

$$-\int \frac{dP_{CO}}{P_{CO}^{(p+q)}} \propto \int dt$$

which means that in a particular experiment we have

$$P_{CO}^{(1-p-q)} \propto t + \text{constant}$$

From the fact given that plots of $P_{CO}^{-1/2}$ against t are linear

$$1 - p - q = -\tfrac{1}{2}$$

Hence $p + q = \frac{3}{2}$ and the overall order of the reaction is $\frac{3}{2}$.

When the ratio of P_{CO} to P_{O_2} is increased substantially in the second set of experiments, this corresponds to the conditions of the isolation method for determining partial orders of a reaction, since P_{CO} is so large with respect to P_{O_2} that it can be considered to remain constant throughout the particular experiment. The overall reaction will then follow the pseudo-q^{th} order kinetics represented by the effective rate law

$$-\frac{1}{2}\frac{dP_{CO}}{dt} = -\frac{dP_{O_2}}{dt} \propto P_{O_2}^{q}$$

Collecting variables and integrating we obtain

$$-\int \frac{dP_{O_2}}{P_{O_2}^q} \propto \int dt$$

and hence

$$P_{O_2}^{(1-q)} \propto t + \text{constant}$$

The linearity of the experimental plots of $P_{O_2}^{1/2}$ versus t shows that $1-q=\frac{1}{2}$, so that $q=\frac{1}{2}$ and since $p+q=\frac{3}{2}$, $p=1$. Thus the reaction is first order in carbon monoxide and one half order in oxygen.

The Eley-Rideal mechanism proposed can be represented as

$$O_2(g) + 2e^- \rightleftharpoons 2O^-_{ads} \quad (1)$$

$$O^-_{ads} + CO(g) \rightarrow CO_2(g) \quad (2)$$

The electron (e^-) concentration at the solid surface can be regarded as constant. Thus if θ is the fraction of potentially-available surface sites occupied by O^-, then the Langmuir adsorption isotherm equates rates of adsorption and desorption on the left and right hand sides respectively as

$$k_1 P_{O_2}(1-\theta)^2 = k_{-1}\theta^2$$

with the squared factors reflecting the necessity that two vacant surface sites are used for adsorption of O_2 and the interaction of two O^-_{ads} species is required for desorption. Rearrangement, taking account that the surface coverage of O^-_{ads} is to be low, i.e. $(1-\theta) \simeq 1$, yields

$$P_{O_2}^{1/2} \propto \theta$$

Now if step (2) is to be considered as rate-determining, the overall rate of reaction will depend on the product of θ (the effective surface concentration of O^-) and the gas phase concentration (partial pressure) of CO, i.e. the rate of the overall reaction will be proportional to $P_{O_2}^{1/2}P_{CO}$ in agreement with the observations.

It is worthwhile noting that a Langmuir-Hinshelwood mechanism would not predict the observed order, since the rate-determining step would in that case be represented as

$$O^-_{ads} + CO_{ads} \rightarrow CO_2(g)$$

Since we are told that CO is very strongly adsorbed by the ZnO surface, then the effective surface concentration of CO will be independent of P_{CO}: with the same oxygen equilibrium occurring at different sites from those at which CO is adsorbed, the overall rate would depend only on $P_{O_2}^{1/2}$, which is in disagreement with the observed rate law.

SECTION NINE

PHOTOCHEMICAL REACTION KINETICS

Example 38

Quantum yield, photodissociation, photochemical rate, Beer–Lambert law, absorbance.

Diazo-n-propane vapour is photodissociated with monochromatic light of wavelength 440 nm according to the process

$$CH_3CH_2CHN_2 + h\nu \rightarrow CH_3CH{=}CH_2 + N_2$$

and the products are transparent at this wavelength. At 298 K, an initial mixture of a partial pressure of 9·31 kPa of diazo-n-propane in nitrogen diluent in a cylindrical cell 100 mm long and 50 mm diameter was photolysed using a beam of monochromatic light of wavelength 440 nm, passing along the axis of the cell with incident intensity of $0{\cdot}67 \times 10^{-7}$ einstein s^{-1}. After irradiation times (t) the absorbance (A) along the same optical path was measured with a weak source of 440 nm light with the following results:

$10^2 A$	7·02	6·31	5·88	5·32
t (s)	0	8499	14085	21974

Devise a function to plot against t so that the gradient will be equal to the quantum yield (ϕ) for the photodissociation and hence evaluate ϕ.

Source: Avila, M. J., Figuera, J. M., Menendez, V. and Perez, J. M. (1976) *Journal of the Chemical Society, Faraday Transactions I*, **72**, p. 422. (Spain)

Solution

The initial concentration of diazo-n-propane (C_o) is given by the ideal gas law as

$$C_o = \frac{P_o}{RT}$$

$$= \frac{9310}{8{\cdot}314 \times 298}$$

$$= 3{\cdot}76 \text{ mol m}^{-3} = 3{\cdot}76 \times 10^{-3} \text{ mol dm}^{-3}.$$

The Beer–Lambert law can be written in the form

$$\frac{I_o}{I_{Tr}} = \exp(\alpha C)$$

where I_o is the incident intensity, I_{Tr} is the intensity transmitted through the cell, α is a constant equal to the product of the exponential absorption coefficient of diazo-n-propane and the optical pathlength through the cell. For the weak beam of light we shall have the absorbance defined by

$$A = \log_{10}\left(\frac{I_o}{I_{Tr}}\right) = \frac{\alpha C}{2{\cdot}303}$$

where C is the concentration of diazo-n-propane at time t. Thus we can evaluate α from the value of A at $t=0$, when we know C_o.

$$\alpha = \frac{0{\cdot}0702 \times 2{\cdot}303}{3{\cdot}76 \times 10^{-3}} = 43{\cdot}0 \text{ dm}^3 \text{ mol}^{-1}$$

Hence we can convert the values of A at other t into values of C:

10^3C (mol dm^{-3})	3·38	3·15	2·85
t (s)	8499	14 085	21 974

For the strong photolysis beam, the Beer–Lambert law gives the intensity absorbed (I_a) as

$$I_a = I_o - I_{Tr} = I_o[1 - \exp(-\alpha C)] \qquad \text{(i)}$$

In a photochemical process where the irradiated substrate decomposes unimolecularly and irreversibly, the rate of substrate destruction can be written as

$$\frac{-dC}{dt} = \frac{\phi I_a}{V} \qquad \text{(ii)}$$

where ϕ is the quantum yield and V is the cell volume (in the present case equal to $\pi(0{\cdot}25)^2 \times 1 = 0{\cdot}196$ dm^3). Substitution of (i) into (ii) yields

$$\frac{-dC}{dt} = \frac{\phi}{V} I_o[1 - \exp(-\alpha C)]$$

Collecting the variables for integration we obtain

$$\int_{C_o}^{C} \frac{-dC}{1 - \exp(-\alpha C)} = \frac{\phi}{V} I_o \int_0^t dt$$

which integrates to yield

$$-[C + \alpha^{-1} \ln\{1 - \exp(-\alpha C)\}]_{C_o}^{C} = \frac{\phi}{V} I_o t$$

Application of the limits on the left hand side and rearrangement yields

$$F = (V/I_o)\{C_o - C + \alpha^{-1} \ln [(1-\exp(-\alpha C_o)]/[1-\exp(-\alpha C)]\} = \phi t$$

where F is the required function which will plot linearly versus t with gradient equal to ϕ, the quantum yield. The data for the plot are as follows:

F (s)	7818	12 957	20 214
t (s)	8499	14 085	21 974

The plot is linear, passing through the origin, and has gradient of $0{\cdot}93 = \phi$.

Example 39

Primary photochemical act, electronic excitation, photo-induced reaction, fluorescence, Stern–Volmer plot, steady state approximation.

When aqueous solutions containing 0·030 mol dm^{-3} of Ce(III), persulphate ions ($S_2O_8^{2-}$) and 0·4 mol dm^{-3} of sulphuric acid were irradiated at a wavelength of 300 nm, Ce(III) was photo-oxidised to Ce(IV) and Ce(III) fluorescence was observed at around 350 nm. The photo-oxidation rate (R) was determined by spectrophotometric absorbance measurements of the concentrations of Ce(III) as a function of time and the fluorescence intensity (F) was also measured. Both R and F were normalised to the values which would have been obtained if the Ce(III), at any particular concentration, had absorbed the same amount of light (i.e. the same rate of excitation of the electronically-excited state of Ce(III) in all solutions).

The following results were obtained, where F_o denotes the fluorescence intensity observed in the absence of persulphate ions:

$10^3[S_2O_8^{2-}]$ (mol dm^{-3})	1·00	2·00	5·00	10·0
F/F_o	0·910	0·835	0·669	0·502
$10^8 R$ (mol dm^{-3} s^{-1})	1·05	1·93	3·87	5·82

Show that these results are consistent with the photo-oxidation being induced by the process whereby $S_2O_8^{2-}$ ions quench fluorescence from the electronically-excited state of Ce(III) produced by absorption of the light.
Source: Matthews, R. W. and Sworski, T. J. (1975) *Journal of Physical Chemistry*, **79**, p. 681. (Australia)

Solution
If we denote the electronically-excited state of Ce(III) produced by absorption of the radiation by Ce(III)*, then the primary photochemical act can be represented as

$$\text{Ce(III)} + h\nu \rightarrow \text{Ce(III)*} \quad (1)$$

We may denote the rate of this process by R^* and because of the normalisation procedure this is the same for all experiments. Fluorescence will result from the process represented as

$$Ce(III)^* \rightarrow Ce(III) + h\nu' \quad (2)$$

Quenching by the medium or some component of it (e.g. H_3O^+ ions), but excluding $S_2O_8^{2-}$ ions may be represented as

$$Ce(III)^* + M \rightarrow Ce(III) + M \quad (3)$$

where M encompasses all effective species and its concentration will be constant for all the solutions considered here. The specific quenching by $S_2O_8^{2-}$ may be represented as

$$Ce(III)^* + S_2O_8^{2-} \rightarrow Ce(IV) + \text{products} \quad (4)$$

anticipating that what we have to prove is that all such quenching acts yield Ce(IV).

We may apply the steady state approximation to Ce(III)*, since its concentration must be very small. Thus we obtain the equation

$$\frac{d[Ce(III)^*]}{dt} = 0 = R^* - [Ce(III)^*](k_2 + k_3[M] + k_4[S_2O_8^{2-}])$$

and on rearrangement

$$[Ce(III)^*] = \frac{R^*}{k_2 + k_3[M] + k_4[S_2O_8^{2-}]}$$

The fluorescence intensity (F) will be expressed as

$$F = k_2[Ce(III)^*]$$

$$= \frac{R^* k_2}{k_2 + k_3[M] + k_4[S_2O_8^{2-}]}$$

while that in the absence of $S_2O_8^{2-}$ ions will be expressed as

$$F_o = \frac{R^* k_2}{k_2 + k_3[M]}$$

The ratio of these fluorescence intensities can then be expressed as

$$\frac{F_o}{F} = 1 + \frac{k_4[S_2O_8^{2-}]}{k_2 + k_3[M]}$$

This then expresses the form of the Stern–Volmer plot, a linear plot of F_o/F

versus the concentration of the quenching agent, $S_2O_8^{2-}$ ions, with gradient in this case of $k_4/(k_2+k_3[M])$. The data for the plot are as follows:

F_o/F	1·10	1·20	1·49	1·99
$10^3[S_2O_8^{2-}]$ (mol dm^{-3})	1·00	2·00	5·00	10·0

This plot is linear with gradient of 99 dm^3 mol^{-1} $=k_4/(k_2+k_3[M])$.

Now if reaction (4) represents the only interaction of Ce(III)* with the $S_2O_8^{2-}$ ion, then the overall rate (R) of photo-oxidation will be determined by the rate of reaction (4). Thus

$$R = k_4[\text{Ce(III)*}][S_2O_8^{2-}]$$

$$= \frac{k_4R^*[S_2O_8^{2-}]}{k_2+k_3[M]+k_4[S_2O_8^{2-}]}$$

$$= \frac{R^*}{1+\dfrac{k_2+k_3[M]}{k_4[S_2O_8^{2-}]}}$$

Hence on inverting both sides of this equation we obtain

$$R^{-1} = R^{*-1}\left(1+\frac{k_2+k_3[M]}{k_4}[S_2O_8^{2-}]^{-1}\right)$$

which predicts a linear plot of R^{-1} versus the reciprocal concentration of $S_2O_8^{2-}$, with intercept to gradient ratio equal to $k_4/(k_2+k_3[M])$. The data for the plot are as follows:

$10^{-7}R^{-1}$ (dm^3 mol^{-1} s)	9·52	5·18	2·58	1·72
$[S_2O_8^{2-}]^{-1}$ (dm^3 mol^{-1})	1000	500	200	100

This plot is linear with gradient of $8{\cdot}67\times10^4$ s and intercept of $0{\cdot}85\times10^7$ dm^3 mol^{-1} s, so that the ratio of the intercept to the gradient is 98 dm^3 mol^{-1} $=k_4/(k_2+k_3[M])$.

The near identity of the values of $k_4/(k_2+k_3[M])$ from the fluorescence and photo-oxidation experiments indicates that reaction (4) represents the total interaction of Ce(III)* with $S_2O_8^{2-}$. If there were an additional interaction which did not give rise to Ce(IV), then the effective value of k_4 in the fluorescence experiments should have been larger than the effective value in the photo-oxidation experiments: the present results indicate only a 1% difference, which cannot be regarded as significant.

SECTION TEN

RADIOLYSIS REACTION KINETICS

Example 40

γ Radiolysis (continuous), *G* value, scavenger usage.

The γ radiolysis of water produces solvated electrons (e^-), hydrogen atoms and hydroxyl radicals available to react with solute molecules. In solutions of dissolved nitrous oxide (N_2O) with concentrations in the range 2×10^{-4} to 2×10^{-3} mol dm^{-3}, the N_2 product *G* value was measured as $G(N_2) = 2{\cdot}7$ at 296 K. In solutions of dissolved sulphur hexafluoride (SF_6) with concentrations in the same range as above, the fluoride ion *G* value was measured as $G(F^-) = 16{\cdot}2$ at 296 K.

Upon addition of $CdCl_2$ to a solution with $[SF_6] = 8{\cdot}0 \times 10^{-4}$ mol dm^{-3} at 296 K, $G(F^-)$ was found to vary as follows:

$10^4[CdCl_2]$ (mol dm^{-3})	0·40	1·00	4·00	10·0	20·0
$G(F^-)$	13·8	11·4	6·0	3·1	1·7

On the other hand, $G(F^-)$ was unaltered when KBr was added to a concentration of 0·1 mol dm^{-3} or when methanol was added to a concentration of 0·1 mol dm^{-3} to the SF_6 solution.

On the basis of the significant reactions for these systems given below, deduce which species reacts with SF_6, the stoichiometric yield of F^- ions resulting from each reaction act and the relative rate constant values which are needed to explain the above data.

$$e^- + N_2O \rightarrow N_2 + O^-$$

$$e^- + CdCl_2 \rightarrow \text{unreactive products (electron scavenging)}$$

$$OH + KBr \rightarrow \text{unreactive products (OH scavenging)}$$

$$H/OH + CF_3OH \rightarrow \text{unreactive products (H/OH scavenging)}$$

Source: Jha, K. N., Ryan, T. G. and Freeman, G. R. (1975) *Journal of Physical Chemistry*, **79**, p. 868. (Canada)

Solution

In N_2O solutions, where $G(N_2)$ is independent of $[N_2O]$, it is clear that $G(N_2)$ is simply equivalent to the yield of electrons, i.e. $G(e^-)=2{\cdot}7$.

In SF_6 solutions, the failure of KBr (OH scavenger) and methanol (H and OH scavenger) to affect $G(F^-)$ clearly indicates that only electrons react with SF_6 to yield F^-, borne out by the decrease in $G(F^-)$ with increasing additions of $CdCl_2$. which does scavenge electrons. Thus the competition in these solutions is clearly between the overall reactions

$$e^- + SF_6 \xrightarrow{k_1} \text{products} + nF^-$$

$$e^- + CdCl_2 \xrightarrow{k_2} \text{scavenged products}$$

Since we have established $G(e^-)=2{\cdot}7$ for water, $n=G(F^-)/G(e^-)=16{\cdot}2/2{\cdot}7=6{\cdot}0$.

It follows then that the yield of F^- for a given $[CdCl_2]$ and $[SF_6]$ will be given by the equation

$$n_a = \frac{6k_1[SF_6]}{k_1[SF_6]+k_2[CdCl_2]}$$

(where n_a is the apparent value of n overall) and taking account that $G(F^-)=16{\cdot}2$ for $[CdCl_2]=0$, we derive the form

$$\frac{G(F^-)}{16{\cdot}2} = \frac{k_1[SF_6]}{k_1[SF_6]+k_2[CdCl_2]}$$

Inversion of both sides of this equation yields the form

$$\frac{16{\cdot}2}{G(F^-)} = 1 + \frac{k_2[CdCl_2]}{k_1[SF_6]}$$

Thus a linear plot of $G(F^-)^{-1}$ versus $[CdCl_2]$ is predicted under the conditions where $[SF_6]=8{\cdot}0\times10^{-4}$ mol dm^{-3} in each experiment and the gradient should be equal to $k_2/(k_1\times16{\cdot}2\times8{\cdot}0\times10^{-4})=77k_2/k_1$. The data for the plot are as follows:

$G(F^-)^{-1}$	0·0617	0·0725	0·0877	0·167	0·323	0·588
$10^4[CdCl_2]$ (mol dm^{-3})	0	0·40	1·00	4·00	10·0	20·0

The plot is linear as required: the gradient is equal to 261 dm^3 mol^{-1} so that $k_2/k_1=261/77=3{\cdot}4$. Thus $CdCl_2$ must react 3·4 times faster than SF_6 at the same concentration with solvated electrons to explain the results given.

Example 41

Pulse radiolysis, dose, *G* value, pseudo-order rate law (for product appearance), absorbance.

Following the pulse radiolysis of oxygenated aqueous solutions containing 0·010 mol dm^{-3} of Cr^{3+} ions and 0·5 mol dm^{-3} of tertiary butanol (the latter present to scavenge OH radicals), an absorption spectrum was detected in the vicinity of 250 nm wavelength and this was ascribed to CrO_2^{2+} ions. The absorbance (A) in this region built up in the early stages after the pulse and eventually reached a limiting value which showed no decay.

In experiments in solutions with $[O_2]=1{\cdot}30\times10^{-3}$ mol dm^{-3}, A was measured as a function of time (t). In the absence of added benzoquinone (Bq) the following results were obtained:

t (μs)	1·60	2·74	4·01	5·58	4500
$10^2 A$	2·18	3·35	4·37	5·30	7·72

With $[Bq]=7{\cdot}0\times10^{-4}$ mol dm^{-3}, A was measured as $3{\cdot}72\times10^{-2}$ at $t=$ 4500 μs.

On the basis that the mechanism involved is as follows:

$$Cr^{3+} + e^- \xrightarrow{\text{fast}} Cr^{2+} \qquad \text{(complete in} \leqslant 1\,\mu s)$$

$$Cr^{2+} + O_2 \longrightarrow CrO_2^{2+} \qquad (1)$$

$$Cr^{2+} + Bq \longrightarrow \text{inert product} \qquad (2)$$

where e^- represents the solvated electron, and with $G(e^-)=2{\cdot}8$ with the absorbed dose per pulse being 510 rad for a solution volume of $1{\cdot}50\times10^{-3}$ dm^3, calculate values for the rate constants for reactions (1) and (2).

Source: Sellers, R. M. and Simic, M. G. (1975) *Journal of the Chemical Society, Chemical Communications*, p. 401. (West Germany)

Solution

The effective initial concentration (at $t\sim1$ μs) of Cr^{2+} in both the experiments is simply equal to that of e^- produced by the pulse. Since 1 rad is defined as 10 μJ of energy absorbed by the water solvent, 510 rad corresponds to $5{\cdot}10\times10^{-3}$ J absorbed per pulse. *G* values are defined as the number of mols of a particular product generated per 100 eV of energy absorbed, i.e. per 96·5 MJ absorbed. Hence with $G(e^-)=2{\cdot}8$, the yield of e^- in the solution is $2{\cdot}8\times5{\cdot}10\times10^{-3}/9{\cdot}65\times10^{6}=1{\cdot}48\times10^{-9}$ mol in a volume of $1{\cdot}50\times10^{-3}$ dm^3. Thus the effective initial $[Cr^{2+}]=1{\cdot}48\times10^{-9}/1{\cdot}50\times10^{-3}=9{\cdot}90\times10^{-7}$ mol dm^{-3}.

Now in the absence of benzoquinone, the only reaction occurring within the observation time-scale will be

$$Cr^{2+} + O_2 \rightarrow CrO_2^{2+} \qquad (1)$$

Hence we shall have the differential rate law

$$\frac{d[CrO_2^{2+}]}{dt} = -\frac{d[Cr^{2+}]}{dt} = k_1[Cr^{2+}][O_2]$$

Also with $[Cr^{2+}] \leqslant 9{\cdot}90 \times 10^{-7}$ mol dm^{-3} and $[O_2] = 1{\cdot}30 \times 10^{-3}$ mol dm^{-3}, it is obvious that $[O_2]$ will remain effectively constant throughout so that the reaction takes place under pseudo-first order conditions. The effective rate law will then take the form

$$\frac{dx}{dt} = {}_1k(a-x)$$

where ${}_1k = k_1[O_2]$ and a represents the initial concentration of Cr^{2+} with x the concentration reacted at time t. In integrated form this becomes

$$\ln \frac{a}{a-x} = {}_1kt$$

Since the absorbance A will be proportional to the concentration of CrO_2^{2+} present at time t (see example 8), $A \propto x$. Also since the final absorbance of the solution, A_f, will be proportional to the concentration of CrO_2^{2+} and hence in this case to the initial concentration of Cr^{2+}, $A_f \propto a$. Thus the above integrated form of the rate law can be written as

$$\ln \frac{A_f}{A_f - A} = {}_1kt$$

Since A changes significantly on a time scale of μs (first four results), A_f can be identified with the absorbance at $t = 4500$ μs. The above equation predicts that a plot of $\ln(A_f - A)$ versus t should be linear with gradient equal to $-{}_1k$. The data for the plot are as follows:

$10^6 t$ (s)	1·60	2·74	4·01	5·58
$\ln(A_f - A)$	−2·893	−3·130	−3·396	−3·721

This plot is linear and from the gradient we derive ${}_1k = 2{\cdot}08 \times 10^5$ s^{-1} $= k_1 \times 1{\cdot}30 \times 10^{-3}$, so that $k_1 = 1{\cdot}60 \times 10^8$ dm^3 mol^{-1} s^{-1}.

In the experiment where benzoquinone is present, there will be competition for the available Cr^{2+} between the two reactions, (1) and

$$Cr^{2+} + Bq \rightarrow \text{product} \qquad (2)$$

Since $[Bq] = 7{\cdot}0 \times 10^{-4}$ mol dm^{-3}, which is also very much larger than the effective initial concentration of Cr^{2+}, both reactions (1) and (2) will take place under pseudo-first order conditions. If we define ${}_1k=k_1[O_2]$ as before and ${}_1k'=k_2[Bq]$, the differential rate law will be

$$\frac{-d[Cr^{2+}]}{dt}=({}_1k+{}_1k')[Cr^{2+}]$$

But only a time-invariant fraction ${}_1k/({}_1k+{}_1k')$ of the Cr^{2+} removed appears as CrO_2^{2+}, so that the limiting concentration of CrO_2^{2+} at $t=4500\mu s$ will be ${}_1ka/({}_1k+{}_1k')$ in the presence of benzoquinone as opposed to a in its absence. It follows that the ratio of the two A_f parameters ($\propto[CrO_2^{2+}]_f$) for the second experiment to the first will simply be equal to ${}_1k/({}_1k+{}_1k')$. Therefore we equate

$$\frac{{}_1k}{{}_1k+{}_1k'}=\frac{3{\cdot}72\times10^{-2}}{7{\cdot}72\times10^{-2}}=0{\cdot}482$$

On rearrangement we obtain ${}_1k'/{}_1k=1{\cdot}08$, and since ${}_1k=2{\cdot}08\times10^5\ s^{-1}$ from the first experiment, ${}_1k'=2{\cdot}25\times10^5\ s^{-1}=k_2$ [Bq]. Therefore we have $k_2=2{\cdot}25\times10^5/7{\cdot}0\times10^{-4}=3{\cdot}2\times10^8\ dm^3\ mol^{-1}\ s^{-1}$.

SECTION ELEVEN

BASIC ELECTROCHEMICAL KINETICS

Example 42

Electrochemical rate, overpotential, polarisation, exchange current, Butler–Volmer equation, isotope exchange.

At a series of established potentials (E) relative to a standard hydrogen electrode ($E^{\ominus}=0$ V by convention), the rate of enrichment of radioactive iron (^{59}Fe) on the surface of an iron electrode was measured, when the radioisotope was present initially only in the contacting solution of Fe^{2+} ions. The fraction of the total radioactivity on the electrode ($\Delta I/I$) of surface area $9{\cdot}1\times10^{-4}$ m^2 increased linearly with time (t) for E in the range -700 mV to -850 mV at 298 K when Fe^{2+} was present at a concentration of $1{\cdot}7\times10^{-6}$ mol dm^{-3} in a solution volume of $1{\cdot}0\times10^{-2}$ dm^3 maintained at pH$=4{\cdot}5$, with gradients measured as follows:

$(\Delta I/I\Delta t)$ (% s^{-1})	0·00861	0·0128	0·0183	0·0427
$-E$(mV)	702	727	752	812

Calculate the magnitudes (i.e. ignoring conventional sign) of the cathodic current densities for the process represented as

$$Fe^{2+}+2e^{-}\rightarrow Fe$$

and hence the exchange current density under these conditions, given that $E^{\ominus}_{Fe^{2+}/Fe}=-0{\cdot}440$ V, on the assumption that corrosion rates are negligible.
Source: Konya, J. (1977) *Journal of Electroanalytical Chemistry*, **84**, p. 83. (Hungary)

Solution
The Nernst Equation predicts the equilibrium (i.e. zero current) potential of the Fe^{2+}/Fe half-cell for the reduction process occurring at the cathode:

(presuming unity activity coefficients in the absence of further information)

$$E = E^{\ominus} + \left(\frac{RT}{zF}\right) \ln [Fe^{2+}]$$

$$= -0{\cdot}440 + \left(\frac{8{\cdot}314 \times 298}{2 \times 96\,494}\right) \ln (1{\cdot}7 \times 10^{-6})$$

$$= -0{\cdot}611 \text{ V}$$

where F is the Faraday (the charge carried by 6×10^{23} electrons = 96 494 coulombs) and $z = 2$, the number of electron equivalents involved per mol of Fe^{2+} reduced. The applied potentials evidently drive the cell in the reverse direction to the spontaneous reaction, so that the net reaction is represented as:

$$Fe^{2+}(aq) + H_2(g) \rightarrow Fe(s) + 2H^+(aq)$$

Under these conditions we may consider the rate of the reverse anodic reaction at the iron electrode (putting Fe into solution) to be negligible in comparison with the rate of the cathodic reaction depositing iron. Accordingly the cathodic current will be effectively equal to the net current. The cathodic current density (i_c) will be given by the high current density form of the Butler–Volmer equation expressed as

$$i_c = i_o \exp - \frac{\beta z F \eta}{RT} \qquad (z = 2 \text{ in this case})$$

The parameter i_o is the exchange current density of the Fe/Fe^{2+} electrode, β is a constant known as the symmetry factor and η is the overpotential which arises from polarisation of the Fe/Fe^{2+} electrode (the complementary hydrogen electrode can be assumed to be unpolarised under normal conditions). The value of the overpotential is given by $\eta = E + 0{\cdot}611$ V here.

The rate of an electrochemical reaction proceeding with a current density i is given by iS/zF, where S is the surface area of the electrode. Hence we have (in the present case where $i \simeq i_c$)

$$i_c = (\text{rate of deposition of Fe}) \times \frac{2F}{S}$$

The fraction of the total ^{59}Fe deposited in unit time ($\Delta I/I \cdot \Delta t$) is taken to be equal to the fraction of all the Fe deposited from the solution in unit time since there will be no isotopic differentiation. In 0·01 dm^3 of solution with $[Fe^{2+}] = 1{\cdot}7 \times 10^{-6}$ mol dm^{-3}, there are $1{\cdot}7 \times 10^{-8}$ mols of Fe^{2+}. From the given data for $E = -702$ mV, the rate of deposition of iron will be given as $8{\cdot}61 \times 10^{-5} \times 1{\cdot}7 \times 10^{-8} = 1{\cdot}47 \times 10^{-12}$ mol s^{-1} so that from the above relationship we derive $i_c = 1{\cdot}47 \times 10^{-12} \times 2 \times 96\,494/9{\cdot}1 \times 10^{-4} = 3{\cdot}1 \times$

10^{-4} A m^{-2}. Similarly other values of i_c are obtained, as tabulated below for each value of E and hence:

$-E$ (mV)	702	727	752	812
$-\eta$ (mV)	91	116	141	201
$10^4 i_c$ (A m^{-2})	3·1	4·6	6·6	15·5

By taking logarithms of the high current form of the Butler–Volmer equation we derive the equation

$$\ln i_c = \ln i_o - \frac{2\beta F\eta}{RT}$$

so that a plot of $\ln i_c$ versus η should be linear (c.f. Tafel Equation form $\eta = a + b \ln i$) and i_o will be equal to i_o when $\eta = 0$. The data to be plotted are as follows:

η (mV)	−91	−116	−141	−201
$\ln i_c$	−8·079	−7·684	−7·323	−6·470

This plot is closely linear and extrapolation to $\eta = 0$ yields $\ln i_o = -9{\cdot}40$ and hence $i_o = 8{\cdot}3 \times 10^{-5}$ A m^{-2}.

Example 43

Electrochemical mechanism, electrochemical experimental rate law, Butler–Volmer equation, Tafel law.

The variations of electrode potential (E) of a nickel electrode in contact with acidic nickel chloride solutions containing a large excess of NaCl (2 mol dm^{-3}) have been measured under conditions where Tafel law equations hold in both anodic and cathodic regimes. The following values of the gradients of linear plots were found at 298 K, where the magnitude of the net current is denoted as $|i|$ and the ionic activity of the ion X is denoted by a_X.

Anodic region

$$\left(\frac{\partial E}{\partial \ln |i|}\right)_{a_{OH^-}} = 0{\cdot}024 \text{ V}, \qquad \left(\frac{\partial E}{\partial \ln a_{OH^-}}\right)_i = -0{\cdot}017 \text{ V}$$

Cathodic region

$$\left(\frac{\partial E}{\partial \ln |i|}\right)_{a_{Ni^{2+}}, a_{OH^-}} = -0{\cdot}051 \text{ V}, \qquad \left(\frac{\partial \ln |i|}{\partial \ln a_{Ni^{2+}}}\right)_{a_{OH^-}, E} = 1{\cdot}0$$

The cathodic process is to be regarded as only depositing nickel.

Which of these values is not in agreement with the predictions to be made on the basis of the following mechanism?

$$Ni(s)+H_2O \rightleftharpoons (NiOH)_{ads}+H^++e^- \quad (1)$$
$$(NiOH)_{ads} \rightleftharpoons NiOH^+(aq)+e^- \quad (2)$$
$$NiOH^+(aq) \rightleftharpoons Ni^{2+}(aq)+OH^-(aq) \quad (3)$$

Step (2) or its reverse denoted as (-2) is to be taken as rate-determining and the adsorbed species denoted as $(NiOH)_{ads}$ is to be considered to achieve only a very small surface coverage on the nickel electrode. The symmetry factor involved can be assumed to have a value of 0·5.

Source: Piatti, R. C. V., Arvia, A. J. and Podesta, J. (1969) *Electrochimica Acta*, **14**, p. 541. (Argentina)

Solution

For the given mechanism with step (2) or (-2) rate-determining and adopting the accepted sign convention for current, we shall have for the overall rate as expressed by the net current density, i, the expression

$$i = zF(R_{-2}+R_2) = 2F(R_{-2}+R_2) \quad \text{(i)}$$

where the R parameters correspond to the rates of the subscripted reaction step and differ in sign.

Clearly the rate of reaction (2) will be proportional to the surface coverage of the species (NiOH), denoted by θ (see example 35). In turn the reverse rate, R_{-2}, will be proportional to $(1-\theta)$, the fraction of surface sites vacant and also to $[NiOH^+(aq)]$. The Butler–Volmer equation developed from equation (i) and incorporating these features then takes the form

$$i = 2F\left\{k_{-2}(1-\theta)[NiOH^+]\exp\left(-\frac{\beta F\,\Delta\phi}{RT}\right) - k_2\theta\exp\left(\frac{(1-\beta)F\,\Delta\phi}{RT}\right)\right\} \quad \text{(ii)}$$

where k_{-2} and k_2 are effective rate constants, β is the symmetry factor, $\Delta\phi$ is the electrical potential difference from the electrode to the bulk solution and $z=1$ for the steps (2) and (-2).

An expression for θ is also obtained from the equilibrium expressed by equation (1), using K_1 to denote the effective equilibrium constant in terms of concentrations, valid since the activity coefficients will have constant values on account of the large and constant [NaCl]

$$K_1(1-\theta)\exp\left(\frac{(1-\beta)F\,\Delta\phi}{RT}\right) = \theta[H^+]\exp\left(-\frac{\beta F\,\Delta\phi}{RT}\right)$$

with $z=1$ for this step also. Since we are told that θ is very small, we can take $(1-\theta)\simeq 1$ and, with rearrangement we obtain

$$\theta=\frac{K_1 \exp\left(\frac{F\,\Delta\phi}{RT}\right)}{[\mathrm{H}^+]}=\left(\frac{K_1}{K_\mathrm{w}}\right)[\mathrm{OH}^-]\exp\left(\frac{F\,\Delta\phi}{RT}\right) \qquad \text{(iii)}$$

where $K_\mathrm{w}=[\mathrm{H}^+][\mathrm{OH}^-]$ is the constant ionic product of water.

At the same time $[\mathrm{NiOH}^+(\mathrm{aq})]$ can be expressed using K_3 as the effective concentration equilibrium constant for the equilibrium represented by equation (3) as

$$[\mathrm{Ni}^{2+}][\mathrm{OH}^-]=K_3[\mathrm{NiOH}^+(\mathrm{aq})] \qquad \text{(iv)}$$

valid for solutions of constant ionic strength as we have here.

Now for the anodic Tafel law regime (i.e. net $\mathrm{Ni(s)}\rightarrow \mathrm{Ni}^{2+}$), the rate R_{-2} can be considered negligible in comparison with R_2 and equation (ii) becomes (with substitution of equation (iii) and $\beta=0{\cdot}5$)

$$|i|=2Fk_2\frac{K_1}{K_\mathrm{w}}[\mathrm{OH}^-]\exp\left(\frac{1{\cdot}5F\,\Delta\phi}{RT}\right)$$

and on taking logarithms we derive

$$\ln|i|=\text{constant}+\ln a_{\mathrm{OH}^-}+\frac{1{\cdot}5F\,\Delta\phi}{RT}$$

Hence since $\partial\,\Delta\phi=\partial E$, the predictions deriving from this equation are

$$\left(\frac{\partial E}{\partial \ln|i|}\right)_{a_{\mathrm{OH}^-}}=\frac{RT}{1{\cdot}5F}$$

$$=\frac{8{\cdot}314\times 298}{1{\cdot}5\times 96\,494}$$

$$=0{\cdot}017\ \mathrm{V}$$

This represents disagreement with the value of 0·024 V measured. Also we have a second prediction

$$\left(\frac{\partial E}{\partial \ln a_{\mathrm{OH}^-}}\right)_i=-\frac{RT}{1{\cdot}5F}=-0{\cdot}017\ \mathrm{V}$$

This is in agreement with the value given.

In the cathodic Tafel law regime, we shall have $R_{-2}\gg R_2$ and hence equation (ii) combined with equation (iv) yields

$$|i|=2Fk_{-2}K_3^{-1}[\mathrm{Ni}^{2+}][\mathrm{OH}^-]\exp\left(-\frac{0{\cdot}5F\,\Delta\phi}{RT}\right)$$

and hence on taking logarithms we derive

$$\ln|i| = \text{constant} + \ln a_{\text{Ni}^{2+}} + \ln a_{\text{OH}^-} - \frac{0{\cdot}5F\,\Delta\phi}{RT}$$

The predictions deriving from this equation for the cathodic regime are

$$\left(\frac{\partial E}{\partial \ln|i|}\right)_{a_{\text{Ni}^{2+}},\, a_{\text{OH}^-}} = -\frac{2RT}{F} = -0{\cdot}051\ \text{V}$$

which represents agreement with the experimental value given and

$$\left(\frac{\partial \ln|i|}{\partial \ln a_{\text{Ni}^{2+}}}\right)_{a_{\text{OH}^-},\, E} = 1{\cdot}0$$

which also represents agreement with the value given.

Thus the only value in disagreement with the predictions of the mechanism given is the first value for the anodic region. It is perhaps worthwhile noting that the authors of the source paper ascribed this disagreement to a hypothesis that the electron transfer in the anodic reaction takes place not on a bare metal surface but on a surface covered by a film of the oxide.

SECTION TWELVE

EXERCISE PROBLEMS

This section presents a wide range of additional exercise examples, involving all of the major topics developed in the preceding worked sections, and again derived from the recent research literature of many countries.

In general, the progression through the problems follows the order of the preceding sections. A back-referencing system is used: each number in bold in the body of the text indicates a worked example in which an aspect of relevance is developed. In a few cases, an aspect is introduced which has not been considered explicitly in the worked examples: an additional keyword is therefore put in brackets at the end of the statement of the problem, so that, through a textbook index, the necessary background can be obtained. Where appropriate, as in most cases, an answer for the problem is given in a list at the end of this section.

Problem 1

The decomposition of oxaloacetic acid (OAA) in aqueous solution has been followed by measuring the evolved partial pressure of CO_2 gas (P) as a function of time (t), when P=0 at t=0 (**1**). In the presence of the cooperating catalysts, Cu^{2+} ions and pyridine, at respective concentrations of $2{\cdot}07 \times 10^{-3}$ and $1{\cdot}50$ mol dm^{-3} in solution of pH=4·5 and at temperature 308 K, the measured values of P in a volume of 0·010 dm^3 above $4{\cdot}0 \times 10^{-3}$ dm^3 of solution, initially containing [OAA]=$7{\cdot}50 \times 10^{-2}$ mol dm^{-3} were as follows:

P (kPa)	9·16	17·23	24·34	30·60	36·11	40·97	45·24	49·00
t (min)	2·5	5·0	7·5	10·0	12·5	15·0	17·5	20·0

Show that the decomposition is first order, evaluate the first order rate constant and show that a unity stoichiometry exists between the amount of OAA decomposed and the amount of CO_2 formed.

(Guggenheim method)

Source: Michaylova, V. and Bontchev, P. R. (1970) *Mikrochimica Acta*, p. 344. (Bulgaria)

Problem 2

The rate of dehydrochlorination of pentachloroethane induced by NaOH in aqueous solution at 293 K has been measured using the change in electrical conductivity of the solution to follow the progress of the elementary reaction represented by the equation

$$C_2HCl_5 + OH^- \rightarrow C_2Cl_4 + H_2O + Cl^-$$

In an experiment when the initial concentrations were $[C_2HCl_5] = 1{\cdot}80 \times 10^{-3}$ mol dm^{-3} and $[OH^-] = 2{\cdot}00 \times 10^{-3}$ mol dm^{-3}, the conductivity (C) of the solution changed as a function of reaction time (t) as follows:

C (arbitrary units)	53·9	45·7	41·1	39·4	35·7
t (s)	0	17·8	39·2	53·0	105

The value of C for a solution of [NaCl) $= 2{\cdot}00 \times 10^{-3}$ mol dm^{-3} was 28·0 in the same arbitrary units.

Evaluate the rate constant **(2)** for the reaction on the basis that it is irreversible. (N.B. partial ionic conductivities are additive and can be expressed as $C_X = [X]C_X^0$, where C_X^0 is a constant, for the ion X.)

Source: Walraevans, R., Trouillet, P. and Devos, A. (1974) *International Journal of Chemical Kinetics*, **6**, p. 777. (Belgium)

Problem 3

The reaction between tris(acetylacetone)chromium (CrA_3) and N-bromosuccinimide (NBS) results in monobromo-substitution of each A ligand and the formation of N-succinimide, with a 1:3 reactant stoichiometry of CrA_3 to NBS. The concentration (x) of the product metal complex as a function of reaction time (t) has been determined spectrophotometrically (at 485 nm) in methyl chloride solution at 273 K, when the initial concentrations were $[CrA_3] = 1{\cdot}00 \times 10^{-2}$ mol dm^{-3} and $[NBS] = 3{\cdot}00 \times 10^{-2}$ mol dm^{-3}, as follows:

$10^3 x$ (mol dm^{-3})	1·13	2·04	2·50	2·97	3·39
t (s)	10	20	26	33	40

Show that these data correspond to a reaction first order in each reactant **(2, 3)** and evaluate the rate constant.

Source: Salaita, G. N. and Al-Odeh, L. A. (1973) *Journal of Inorganic and Nuclear Chemistry*, **35**, p. 2116. (Jordan)

Problem 4

The oxidation of dimethyl sulphoxide ($(CH_3)_2SO$) to dimethylsulphone ($(CH_3)_2SO_2$) by permanganate (MnO_4^-) in acidic aqueous solution proceeds according to the stoichiometry

$$(CH_3)_2SO + 2MnO_4^- + 2H^+ \rightarrow (CH_3)_2SO_2 + H_2O + \text{Mn products}$$

In solutions of pH $= 1{\cdot}0$ and ionic strength 1·0 mol dm^{-3}, the rate of removal of MnO_4^- has been followed spectrophotometrically using a stopped flow system. For the initial compositions given below, the decay followed a first order rate law, $-d[MnO_4^-]/dt = k_{obs}[MnO_4^-]$, and the values of the observed rate constant, k_{obs}, were as follows **(2)**:

k_{obs} (s^{-1})	1·24	2·48	0·31	0·62
$10^5[MnO_4^-]$ (mol dm^{-3})	3·0	3·0	30	30
$10^2[(CH_3)_2SO]$ (mol dm^{-3})	1·20	2·40	0·30	0·60

Calculate, on the basis of the above stoichiometry and rate information, the time which will be required for half of the MnO_4^- concentration to be removed in a solution of pH = 1·0 and ionic strength = 1·0 mol dm^{-3} at the same temperature, when the initial concentrations are $3{\cdot}0 \times 10^{-3}$ mol dm^{-3} for each reactant **(3)**, assuming that the reaction mechanism is unchanged.
Source: de Oliveira, L. A., Toma, H. E. and Giesbrecht, E. (1976) *Inorganic and Nuclear Chemistry Letters*, **12**, p. 195. (Brazil)

Problem 5
The rate of reduction of phenyldiazonium borofluoride ($PhN_2^+BF_4^-$) by hypophosphorous acid (H_3PO_2) in 1:1 aqueous acetonitrile solution has been studied, measuring the rate of production of benzene, the sole organic product, using nuclear magnetic resonance detection. The initial rate (R_i) had the values below at a temperature of 316 K as a function of the reactant concentrations:

Experiment number	1	2	3	4	5	6	7
$[PhN_2^+BF_4^-]$ (mol dm^{-3})	0·050	0·12	0·31	0·40	0·40	0·40	0·40
$[H_3PO_2]$ (mol dm^{-3})	2·15	2·15	2·15	2·15	0·43	1·10	2·90
R_i (mol dm^{-3} s^{-1})	0·16	0·59	2·46	3·60	0·72	1·84	4·86

Deduce (*a*) the partial orders of reaction **(4)** for both reactants and (*b*) the value of the rate constant in appropriate units for the overall order of the reaction at 316 K.
Source: Levit, A. F., Kiprianova, L. A. and Gragerov, I. P. (1973) *Doklady Physical Chemistry* (English translation of *Doklady Akademii Nauk S.S.S.R.*), **213**, p. 634. (U.S.S.R.)

Problem 6
The acetal 2-phenyl-1,3-dioxalane (Ac) is reduced by borane (BH_3) in tetrahydrofuran solution to yield an alcohol with unity stoichiometry. At 273 K, the times taken to form $0{\cdot}2 \times 10^{-3}$ mol (t_1) and $0{\cdot}5 \times 10^{-3}$ mol (t_2) of the alcohol product in 0·50 dm^3 of the solution with initial [Ac] = 0·208 mol dm^{-3} for various initial $[BH_3]$ were as follows:

$[BH_3]$ (mol dm^{-3})	1·15	0·95	0·75	0·60	0·40	0·30
t_1 (min)	2·40					101
t_2 (min)	5·90	10·1	19·5	36·4	113	254

These times were doubled when the initial [Ac] was halved at the same $[BH_3]$.
Deduce the order of the reaction and evaluate its rate constant at 273 K expressed in appropriate units, establishing the applicability of the initial rates method to these data **(4)**.
Source: Bolker, H. I. and Fleming, B. I. (1975) *Canadian Journal of Chemistry*, **53**, p. 2818. (Canada)

Problem 7
The catalysed decomposition of hydroxylamine (NH_2OH) in aqueous KOH solutions gives rise to nitrogen, ammonia, nitrous oxide and hyponitrite as reaction products. At 293 K, $[NH_2OH]$ was measured as a function of reaction time (t) in solutions with various (constant) $[OH^-]$ (i.e. OH^- is not consumed in the reaction), starting with

$[NH_2OH] = 2{\cdot}79$ mol dm^{-3} at $t = 0$, yielding the following array of values of $[NH_2OH]$ (mol dm^{-3}):

	Experiment number	1	2	3	4
	$[OH^-]$ (mol dm^{-3})	0·81	2·01	2·61	3·21
t (h)	1·0	2·75	2·27	1·78	1·21
	2·0	2·72	1·85	1·14	0·527
	3·0	2·68	1·51	0·728	0·229
	4·0	2·64	1·23	0·465	0·0995

Evaluate the orders of the reaction in NH_2OH and OH^- (**1, 2, 5**) on the assumption that these are integral.

Source: Lunak, S. and Veprek-Siska, J. (1974) *Collection of Czechoslovak Chemical Communications*, **39**, p. 391. (Czechoslovakia)

Problem 8

The hydrogenation of toluene vapour to methylcyclohexane takes place in the presence of a nickel/zinc oxide catalyst according to the overall reaction represented as

$$C_7H_8 + 3H_2 \rightarrow C_7H_{14}$$

With a sample of the catalyst in a static constant volume reactor at 489 K, the rate of toluene consumption can be deduced from the rate of total pressure decrease. Starting with a partial pressure of toluene of 1·800 kPa and partial pressures of hydrogen of 49·5 kPa (experiment I) and 67·1 kPa (experiment II) (**5**), the following partial pressures (P) of toluene as a function of reaction time (t) were found:

t (min)	5·00	10·0	18·0	25·0	
P (kPa)	1·646	1·498	1·276	1·097	Experiment I
P (kPa)	1·427	1·097	0·659		Experiment II

Addition of methylcyclohexane at the start of reaction did not affect the rate (**7**).

Deduce the partial orders of the reaction (integral or half order) (**4**, [**37**]) and evaluate the rate constant in appropriate units.

(Hint: An estimate of a reaction order q can be obtained by assuming

$$-\frac{\Delta P}{\Delta t} \propto P_{Av}^{q}$$

where Δ represents finite changes in the parameters and P_{Av} is the arithmetical mean of P over the time interval Δt)

Source: Mamaladze, L. M. and Kiperman, S. L. (1975) *Kinetics and Catalysis* (English translation of *Kinetika i Kataliz*), **16**, p. 1501. (U.S.S.R.)

Problem 9

The reaction of imidazole (Im) with benzoyl fluoride (BF) in acetonitrile solvent has been studied by measuring the rate of disappearance of the BF absorption band at 265 nm wavelength when BF concentrations were of the order of 10^{-4} mol dm^{-3}. When $[Im] \geqslant 0{\cdot}01$ mol dm^{-3} (**2**), the decay of [BF] was found to follow first order kinetics and the observed first order rate constant, k_{obs}, varied with [Im] as follows at 298 K:

[Im] (mol dm^{-3})	0·0100	0·0200	0·0427	0·0683	0·0900	0·100
$10^3 k_{obs}$ (s^{-1})	0·0230	0·101	0·553	1·68	3·31	4·31

Show that these results cannot be represented by a rate law of a single order in Im but can be represented by a rate law corresponding to a mechanism of competitive reactions of integral orders in Im (**4**). Evaluate the rate constants involved.
Source: Rogne, O. (1975) *Journal of the Chemical Society, Chemical Communications*, p. 25. (Norway)

Problem 10
The reaction of propylene gas with ozone in ozonised oxygen has been studied in a closed spherical reactor (stainless steel) of internal volume 220 m^3. The intensity of the mercury line at a wavelength of 253·7 nm transmitted along an absorption path of length 17·88 m was used to measure the concentration of ozone as a function of time, the decadic molar absorption coefficient (**8**) of ozone at this wavelength being 30 200 $dm^2\ mol^{-1}$, while oxygen and propylene and reaction products are transparent. At a temperature of 337 K, on introducing a pressure of 20·2 Pa of ozonised oxygen, the fractional absorption, (A'), i.e. the fraction of the incident light intensity absorbed, was $8{\cdot}47 \times 10^{-2}$. Subsequently a partial pressure of 0·798 Pa of propylene was introduced and A' varied as a function of time (t) after contact as follows:

$10^2 A'$	5·99	4·26	2·96	2·08	1·45
t (min)	1·0	2·0	3·0	4·0	5·0

Mass spectrometric analysis showed that the rates of removal of ozone and propylene were equal.

Calculate (a) the concentration ratio of propylene to ozone at $t=0$ and (b) the rate constant for reaction between ozone and propylene assuming that the initial bimolecular step is rate-determining (**2**).

Source: Becker, K. H., Schurath, U. and Seitz, H. (1974) *International Journal of Chemical Kinetics*, **6**, p. 725. (West Germany)

Problem 11
The reaction of ascorbic acid (AA) with 2,6-dichlorophenolindophenol (DCPI) in oxalic acid solutions proceeds irreversibly with unity stoichiometry. In stopped-flow experiments, the transmitted intensity of light of wavelength 522 nm (absorbed only by DCPI) was measured by the output signal (V) of a photomultiplier with a linear response to intensity. An oscilloscope was used to display V as a function of time (t)—dV/dt was always measured at $V=300$ mV when the measured absorbance of the solution was 0·430 (**8**). With an initial concentration, $[\mathrm{DCPI}]_o = 1{\cdot}00 \times 10^{-4}$ mol dm^{-3}, values of dV/dt as a function of the initial concentration of AA, $[\mathrm{AA}]_o$, were as follows:

dV/dt (Vs^{-1})	16·7	50·1	83·5
$10^3[\mathrm{AA}]_o$ (mol dm^{-3})	1·00	3·00	5·00

In a second experiment in the same medium with $[\mathrm{DCPI}]_o = 5{\cdot}00 \times 10^{-6}$ mol dm^{-3} and $[\mathrm{AA}]_o = 1{\cdot}00 \times 10^{-5}$ mol dm^{-3}, the following set of instantaneous values of [DCPI] at various times (t) were measured:

10^6[DCPI] (mol dm^{-3})	3·75	3·17	2·74	2·19
t (s)	0·55	0·90	1·23	1·76

By evaluating the rate constants for a reaction first order in each reactant **(2)**, confirm that the same reaction is occurring in both experiments.
Source: Karayannis, M. I. (1976) *Talanta*, **23**, p. 27. (Greece)

Problem 12
In aqueous solutions of Cr^{3+} ions, the addition of phosphoric acid (H_3PO_4) causes complex formation represented by the equation

$$Cr^{3+} + HPO_4^{2-} \rightarrow CrHPO_4^{+}$$

The optical density (A) **(8)** of newly-mixed solutions containing initially 0·020 mol dm^{-3} of Cr^{3+} and 0·024 mol dm^{-3} of H_3PO_4 at pH = 1·56 has been followed as a function of time (t) using an ultraviolet wavelength where H_3PO_4 and its deprotonated ions are transparent. The results obtained were as follows:

t (h)	0	70	98	142	219	335	407
A	0·315	0·341	0·351	0·367	0·395	0·437	0·463

On the assumption that only the above reaction is occurring in the solution, show that it follows zero order kinetics.
Source: Lahiri, S. C. (1975) *Journal of the Indian Chemical Society*, **52**, p. 478. (India)

Problem 13
The ions biphenyl$^+$ and Cl^- have been produced concurrently by subjecting biphenyl dissolved in 1,2-dichloroethane to a short electron pulse. The concentration, [b], of biphenyl$^+$ was followed spectrophotometrically as a function of time (t) after the pulse, producing the following results:

10^6[b] (mol dm^{-3})	3·45	1·46	0·833	0·534	0·365	0·258	0·187
$10^6 t$ (s)	0	2·6	5·2	7·8	10·4	13·0	15·6

If the bimolecular process

$$\text{biphenyl}^+ + Cl^- \rightarrow \text{inert products}$$

is solely responsible for the decay **(2)**, show that a plot of $1/[b]_1$ versus $1/[b]_2$, where $[b]_1$ and $[b]_2$ are pairs of consecutive concentrations measured with a constant time interval (as above), will allow evaluation of the bimolecular rate constant and the initial concentration of Cl^-. Calculate the values corresponding to the above results.
Source: Shank, N. E. (1973) *International Journal of Chemical Kinetics*, **5**, p. 577. (Zambia)

Problem 14
The polycondensation of succinic acid (HOOC.$(CH_2)_2$.COOH) with ethylene glycol ($(CH_2OH)_2$) at 468 K has been investigated under equimolar conditions (r= $[\text{glycol}]_o/[\text{acid}]_o = 1$) and non-equimolar conditions with r = 1·600. The progress of the unity stoichiometric reaction was followed as a function of time (t) by withdrawal of samples and titration with standardised KOH solution to obtain the corresponding acid molality, C. The results obtained in two experiments were as follows:

$r = 1$	t (min)	0	30	60	120
	C (equiv-mol kg^{-1})	11·0973	2·8283	2·0332	1·4499
$r =$	t (min)	0	60	120	180
	C (equiv-mol kg^{-1})	9·2187	1·3339	0·5006	0·2149

By establishing the linearity of suitable plots of a function of $P=(C_o-C)/C_o$ (where C_o is the equivalent-molality of the acid at $t=0$) or P and r versus t, demonstrate that this reaction follows kinetics which are first order in succinic acid and second order in ethylene glycol for both values of r **(4)**.

Note:

$$\int_{x_1}^{x_2} \frac{dx}{(1-x)(a-x)^2} = (a-1)^{-2}\left[\ln\left(\frac{a-x}{1-x}\right) - \frac{a-1}{a-x}\right]_{x_1}^{x_2}$$

where a is a constant.

Source: Lin, C. C. and Yu, P. C. (1978) *Journal of Polymer Science*, **16**, p. 1005. (Taiwan)

Problem 15

When acetone vapour in a cell is subjected to a short (1 μs) pulse of electrons of energy sufficient to produce only $(CH_3)_2CO^+$ and CH_3CO^+ as primary ions, the positive ions can be trapped in the negative space charge of a low energy electron beam. Sampling from this "bottled" region can be achieved by a short positive voltage pulse applied some time (t) after the initial pulse, with mass spectrometric determination of ion concentrations.

The secondary ion, $(CH_3)_2COH^+$, is generated by the very rapid reaction

$$CH_3CO^+ + (CH_3)_2CO \rightarrow (CH_3)_2COH^+ + CH_2CO$$

and over a longer time scale its concentration decayed to give linear plots of $\ln[(CH_3)_2COH^+]$ versus t **(1)**, with gradients (G) which depended upon [acetone] as follows at 298 K:

$-G$ (s^{-1})	29·0	86·0	216·0	464·6
10^8 [acetone] (mol dm^{-3})	1·1	1·9	3·0	4·4

Assuming that ion concentrations are very much lower than [acetone] **(5)**, deduce an elementary reaction which could explain this decay **(21)** and calculate its rate constant. At what value of mass/charge (m/e) number would you expect to be able to detect the product of this reaction using the mass spectrometer?

(Mass spectrometry, mass/charge number of ions)

Source: Blair, A. S. and Harrison, A. G. (1973) *Canadian Journal of Chemistry*, **51**, p. 703. (Canada)

Problem 16

The oxidation of Sb(III) ions by peroxysulphate ions ($S_2O_8^{2-}$) in aqueous solution proceeds according to the stoichiometric equation:

$$Sb(III) + S_2O_8^{2-} \rightarrow Sb(V) + 2SO_4^{2-}$$

At a temperature of 308 K, in solutions of constant ionic strength, when the initial concentrations of both reactant ions were equal, plots of ln [Sb(III)] versus time (t) were linear **(1)**. When the initial concentration of $S_2O_8^{2-}$ was $1{\cdot}00 \times 10^{-2}$ mol dm^{-3}, the concentration of Sb(III) ions decreased with time as follows:

10^4[Sb(III)] (mol dm^{-3})	2·50	1·96	1·49	1·08	0·741	0·464	0·251
t (min)	0	10	20	30	40	50	60

Additions of Sb(V) and/or SO_4^{2-} to the initial reaction mixture had no effect on the rate.

Show that these data are consistent with a reaction which is kinetically of half order in each reactant and evaluate the first order rate constant (**4**, [**37**]).

Source: Bhargava, A. P. and Gupta, Y. K. (1969) *Zeitschrift fur Physikalische Chemie* (Leipzig), **242**, p. 327. (India)

Problem 17

The vanadyl ion (VO^{2+}) forms a 1:1 complex with pyrophosphate ions ($H_xP_2O_7^{x-2}$) rapidly on mixing the separate solutions. The kinetics have been studied using a stopped-flow apparatus, where equal volumes of solutions of VO^{2+} ($1{\cdot}24 \times 10^{-3}$ mol dm^{-3}) and pyrophosphate ($2{\cdot}4 \times 10^{-2}$ mol dm^{-3}) (**2**) were rapidly dispensed from syringes (coupled) and mixed into a quartz optical cell. An optical path through this cell of length 50 mm was created by mirror reflections and measurements of the ratio of transmitted (I_{Tr}) and incident (I_o) radiation intensities (**8**) at a wavelength of 240 nm as a function of time (t) after mixing were as follows at a temperature of 285 K and solution pH = 2:

I_{Tr}/I_o	0·4650	0·4399	0·4268	0·4119	0·3976	0·3897	0·3761	0·3631	0·3400
t (ms)	0	1·34	2·20	3·35	4·75	5·69	7·75	10·70	∞

The value of I_{Tr}/I_o at $t = \infty$ was invariant for pyrophosphate concentrations increased by an order of magnitude for the same [VO^{2+}] initially.

Given that the reaction is first order in each reactant (**1**), calculate the rate constant for formation of the complex indicated by the above data.

Source: Hoffman, M. R., Stern, R. A., Rieger, P. H. and Edwards, J. O. (1976) *Inorganica Chimica Acta*, **19**, p. 181. (U.S.A.)

Problem 18

Peracetic acid (PA) vapour at ~2% by volume in N_2 carrier gas at total pressure of $1{\cdot}01 \times 10^5$ Pa has been flowed through teflon tubing of uniform internal radius, r (**6**). The gas was sampled at a point 1·20 m downstream from the injection point, with the tubing maintained at a temperature of 490 K along the length. The variation of the fraction (f) of the entry [PA] which was decomposed as a function of total gas flow rate (F) and for tubings of different r was as follows:

f	0·654	0·422	0·282	0·844	0·574	0·385	0·811	0·615	0·458
F (μmol s^{-1})	18·4	35·7	59·1	23·9	52·2	91·5	79·7	142	223
r (mm)	1·40	1·40	1·40	2·50	2·50	2·50	5·00	5·00	5·00

Show that the decomposition follows first order kinetics in each tubing. Evaluate the rate constants at 490 K for each r. Show that these indicate competing homogeneous and heterogeneous decomposition processes and, presuming that each teflon surface has the same heterogeneous characteristics, evaluate the rate constant for the homogeneous process.

Source: Levush, S. S., Prisyazhnyuk, Z. P., Shevchuk, V. U. and Garbuzyuk, I. A. (1975) *Kinetics and Catalysis* (English translation of *Kinetika i Kataliz*), **16**, p. 16. (U.S.S.R.)

Problem 19

A mixture of 1·00% of tertiarybutanol (B) vapour and 0·50% of cyclohexene (C) vapour in argon was introduced to a total pressure of 4·660 kPa at a temperature of 300 K into a "single pulse" shock tube. Gases were sampled through a port in the end-face of the shock tube and gas chromatographic analyses gave integrated peak areas proportional to the concentrations. When a reflected shock wave was created, the products isobutene (I) and ethylene (E) were detected with concentrations varying with reaction time (t) as follows:

t (μs)	200	400	600	800
10^6[I] (mol dm^{-3})	0·64	1·27	1·91	2·54
10^6[E] (mol dm^{-3})	1·14	2·28	3·41	4·53

A pressure transducer showed that total pressure had increased to 106·4 kPa after the shock wave reflection (it remained constant during the reaction times above).

The unimolecular reactions involved are represented as **(1)**

$$B \xrightarrow{k_B} I + H_2O$$
$$C \xrightarrow{k_C} E + \text{1,3-butadiene}$$

and k_C is known to be given by $2{\cdot}01 \times 10^{15} \exp(-33\,670\ \mathrm{K}/T)\ \mathrm{s}^{-1}$ **(5)**. Assuming that isothermal conditions prevail for $t \leqslant 800$ μs, calculate the temperature T attained and the corresponding value of the rate constant k_B.

(Shock tube, reflected shock wave)

Source: Lewis, D., Keil, M. and Sarr, M. (1974) *Journal of the American Chemical Society*, **96**, p. 4398. (U.S.A.)

Problem 20

The rate of oxalate ($C_2O_4^{2-}$) ion disappearance in fused alkali nitrate melts containing dissolved dichromate ($Cr_2O_7^{2-}$) ions has been measured, when the overall reaction is represented by the equation:

$$C_2O_4^{2-} + Cr_2O_7^{2-} + NO_3^- \rightarrow 2CO_2(g) + NO_2^- + 2CrO_4^{2-}$$

Plots of ln [$C_2O_4^{2-}$] (concentration measured by withdrawal of small samples, solution in water and titration) against time were linear **(1)** with gradients (G) as follows, under conditions where [$C_2O_4^{2-}$]$\ll$[$Cr_2O_7^{2-}$]:

$-G$ (min^{-1})	1·09	0·451	0·274	0·137	0·274	0·523
[$Cr_2O_7^{2-}$] (mol kg^{-1})	0·36	0·36	0·36	0·25	0·25	0·25
[CrO_4^{2-}] (mol kg^{-1})	0·09	0·14	0·18	0·15	0·15	0·15
T (K)	548	548	548	528	548	568

Show that these results are consistent with a mechanism written as

$$Cr_2O_7^{2-} + NO_3^- \overset{K}{\rightleftharpoons} 2\,CrO_4^{2-} + NO_2^+$$

$$NO_2^+ + C_2O_4^{2-} \xrightarrow{_2k} 2\,CO_2 + NO_2^-$$

where K is an equilibrium constant and $_2k$ the rate constant for the rate-determining step **(12)**. If it is assumed that K is invariant with temperature (T) in the range involved here, obtain a value for the activation energy **(5)** of the rate-determining step.

Source: Vilcu, R. and Georgescu, N. (1972) *Revue Roumaine de Chimie*, **17**, p. 1669. (Roumania)

Problem 21

The thermal cis ↔ trans isomerisation of the chromium complex $Cr(tfa)_3$ (tfa is the anion of 1,1,1-trifluoro-2,4-pentanedione) has been studied in the gas phase and is a homogeneous process. In a closed glass vessel maintained at a temperature of 418 K and starting with a concentration of $3{\cdot}9 \times 10^{-6}$ mol dm^{-3} of pure cis isomer, the following ratios of trans to cis isomer concentrations ([trans]/[cis]) as a function of reaction time (t) were measured using gas chromatographic analysis:

t (min)	10	20	30	40	∞
[trans]/[cis]	0·316	0·987	1·28	2·00	4·00

Evaluate the rate constants in the forward (cis to trans) and reverse directions (7) for the opposing first order reactions concerned.
Source: Kutal, C. and Sievers, R. E. (1974) *Inorganic Chemistry*, **13**, p. 897. (U.S.A.)

Problem 22

Acrylic acid (AA) has been esterified with methanol (M) solvent in the presence of monoalkyl sulphuric acid as catalyst and triethylamine as the inhibitor of polymerisation, methyl acrylate (E) and water being the only products. With small concentrations of catalyst and inhibitor and starting with [M] = 21·19 mol dm^{-3} and [AA] = 1·073 mol dm^{-3}, the following values of [E] were measured as a function of reaction time (t) at a temperature of 337 K:

[E] (mol dm^{-3})	0	0·0961	0·183	0·330	0·533	0·789
t (min)	0	10·0	20·0	40·0	80·0	∞

Demonstrate that these data are consistent with reversible second order reactions (7) and calculate values for the rate constants.
Source: Malshe, V. C. and Chandalia, S. B. (1977) *Chemical Engineering Science*, **32**, p. 1530. (India)

Problem 23

The equilibrium between the nickel malate (mal) complex and the separate ions

$$Ni(mal) \rightleftharpoons Ni^{2+} + mal^{2-}$$

has been established in aqueous solutions of constant ionic strength under an applied pressure of 25 atmospheres at a temperature of 298 K. Upon suddenly rupturing a diaphragm, the pressure dropped to 1 atmosphere and the relaxation of the equilibrium was observed by electrical conductivity measurements, which gave a profile of the concentration displacement from the final equilibrium position against time. The derived characteristic relaxation time (τ) **(8)** varied as a function of the total added nickel malate concentration as follows:

$10^3\tau$ (s)	14·9	6·17	3·53	2·11
10^4[Ni(mal)] (mol dm^{-3})	1·10	6·80	20·7	58·5

The equilibrium constant, $K = [Ni(mal)]/[Ni^{2+}][mal^{2-}]$ had a value of $3{\cdot}30 \times \times 10^4$ dm^3 mol^{-1} under these final conditions.

Calculate the values of the rate constants for formation and dissociation of the Ni(mal) complex.

(Pressure jump method)

Source: Harada, S. and Yasunaga, T. (1972) *Bulletin of the Chemical Society of Japan*, **45**, p. 1752. (Japan)

Problem 24

When dilute aqueous solutions of scandium(III) ions at a temperature of 298 K were subjected to an electric field jump by the sudden application of a constant high voltage across two platinum electrodes, the conductivity of the solution increased due to a small shift in the equilibrium represented as

$$Sc(H_2O)_6^{3+} \underset{k_b}{\overset{k_f}{\rightleftharpoons}} Sc(H_2O)_5OH^{2+} + H^+$$

Characteristic relaxation times (τ) were obtained as a function of the total concentration of Sc(III) initially added ($[Sc]_T$) and a glass electrode was used to measure the pH of the relaxed solution. The results were as follows:

pH	5·010	4·876	4·461	4·354
$10^5[Sc]_T$ (mol dm^{-3})	1·05	3·16	5·26	8·95
τ (μs)	2·99	2·09	1·57	1·17

An independent measurement of the equilibrium constant with the same electric field applied yielded $K = 1{\cdot}70 \times 10^{-5}$ mol dm^{-3} at 298 K.

Calculate values of the rate constants k_f and k_b **(8)** and show that they are consistent with the value of K given above, assuming that all activity coefficients are unity.

(Electric field jump method)

Source: Cole, D. L., Rich, L. D., Owen, J. D. and Eyring, E. M. (1969) *Inorganic Chemistry*, **8**, p. 682. (U.S.A.)

Problem 25

When succinimide (SI) at initial concentration of $4{\cdot}00 \times 10^{-3}$ mol dm^{-3} was hydrolysed in aqueous solution containing $[OH^-] = 0{\cdot}500$ mol dm^{-3} at a temperature of 333 K, succinamic acid (SA) was a metastable intermediate product and ammonia was a final product, formed by irreversible pseudo-first order reactions and with unity stoichiometry according to the effective reaction scheme **(9)**

$$SI \xrightarrow{k_1} SA \xrightarrow{k_2} NH_3$$

The time required for half-consumption **(5)** of the initial concentration of SI was $8{\cdot}74 \times 10^3$ s, when the yield of NH_3 corresponded to a concentration of 11·7% of the initial [SI]. Calculate the values of the pseudo-first order rate constants k_1 and k_2. (Suggestion—use a numerical iteration method to solve the equation).

Source: Khan, M. N. and Khan, A. A. (1975) *Journal of Organic Chemistry*, **40**, p. 1793. (India)

Problem 26

Diethyl adipate (DA) is saponified (hydrolysed) in two irreversible elementary stages by sodium hydroxide, represented by the equations

$$(CH_2)_4(COOC_2H_5)_2 + OH^- \xrightarrow{k_1} (C_2H_5OOC)(CH_2)_4(COO^-) + C_2H_5OH \quad (1)$$

$$(C_2H_5OOC)(CH_2)_4(COO^-) + OH^- \xrightarrow{k_2} (CH_2)_4(COO^-)_2 + C_2H_5OH \quad (2)$$

The Arrhenius forms for the second order rate constants (**5**) are known to be:

$$k_1 = 4{\cdot}9 \times 10^6 \exp(-5080\ \mathrm{K}/T)\ \mathrm{dm^3\ mol^{-1}\ s^{-1}}$$

$$k_2 = 3{\cdot}5 \times 10^6 \exp(-3010\ \mathrm{K}/T)\ \mathrm{dm^3\ mol^{-1}\ s^{-1}}$$

Equal flow rates on a volume basis of 0·010 $dm^3\ s^{-1}$ of 0·50 mol dm^{-3} NaOH and 0·020 mol dm^{-3} DA aqueous solutions were mixed at entry to a 6·4 mm internal diameter, uniform copper tube, 45 m long (**6**). On the assumptions of plug-flow (i.e. non-turbulent) and isothermal operation, calculate the temperature at which the tube must be maintained to achieve 95% saponification of the DA at the tube exit (**9**). (The use of aqueous solvent limits the temperature range to be considered.)
Source: Newberger, M. R. and Kadlec, R. H. (1973) *A.I.Ch.E. Journal*, **19**, p. 1272. (U.S.A.)

Problem 27
In aqueous solution, the rates of the reaction represented by the overall stoichiometric equation

$$2\mathrm{V(IV)} + \mathrm{Cl_2} \rightarrow 2\mathrm{V(V)} + 2\mathrm{Cl^-}$$

were obtained at constant ionic strength and pH at a temperature of 298 K, by measuring the concentration of V(V) as a function of time spectrophotometrically, and deducing the other concentrations from the stoichiometry.

With initial concentrations of $[\mathrm{V(IV)}]_o = 5{\cdot}60 \times 10^{-3}$ mol dm^{-3} and $[\mathrm{Cl_2}]_o = 2{\cdot}10 \times 10^{-4}$ mol dm^{-3}, a plot of ln $[\mathrm{Cl_2}]$ versus time was linear (**2**) with a gradient of $-0{\cdot}153\ \mathrm{s^{-1}}$.

When the initial concentrations were $[\mathrm{V(IV)}]_o = 1{\cdot}03 \times 10^{-3}$ mol dm^{-3} and $[\mathrm{Cl_2}] = 1{\cdot}31 \times 10^{-3}$ mol dm^{-3}, a plot of ln $\{[\mathrm{Cl_2}]/(\mathrm{V(IV)}]\}$ versus time (**3**) showed a smoothly-decreasing gradient with increasing time, which back-extrapolated to an initial gradient of 0·0436 s^{-1}. When $[\mathrm{V(V)}] = 2{\cdot}0 \times 10^{-4}$ mol dm^{-3} was added to the same initial solution, the initial gradient of the corresponding plot was found to be 0·0144 s^{-1}. On the other hand, addition of Cl^- had no effect (**7**).

Interpret these results in terms of a mechanism (**10**) composed of the minimum number of steps involving single electron transfers and the reactive intermediate species Cl_2^-. Evaluate the elementary step rate constants or their ratios as far as possible.
Source: Adegite, A. (1975) *Journal of the Chemical Society, Dalton Transactions*, p. 1199. (Nigeria)

Problem 28
The reaction between carbon monoxide, fluorine and oxygen in a closed reaction vessel proceeds according to the homogeneous mechanism

$$\mathrm{CO} + \mathrm{F_2} \rightarrow \mathrm{FCO\cdot} + \mathrm{F\cdot} \qquad (1)$$

$$\mathrm{F\cdot} + \mathrm{CO} + \mathrm{M} \rightarrow \mathrm{FCO\cdot} + \mathrm{M} \qquad (2)$$

$$\mathrm{FCO\cdot} + \mathrm{F_2} \rightarrow \mathrm{F_2CO} + \mathrm{F\cdot} \qquad (3)$$

$$\mathrm{FCO\cdot} + \mathrm{O_2} \rightarrow \mathrm{FCO_3\cdot} \qquad (4)$$

$$2\mathrm{FCO_3\cdot} \rightarrow \mathrm{(FCO)_2O_2} + \mathrm{O_2} \qquad (5)$$

Devise a rate law relating the rate of CO consumption to [CO], $[F_2]$ and $[O_2]$ (**10**) and show that this is independent of [M], the sum of the concentrations of all species present.

At a temperature of 294 K, the following variations in the rate of CO consumption with concentrations were observed:

$10^8(-d[CO]/dt)$ (mol dm^{-3} s^{-1})	9·02	64·2	357	326
10^4[CO] (mol dm^{-3})	9·70	16·0	19·7	25·6
$10^4[F_2]$ (mol dm^{-3})	1·45	3·84	12·3	7·14
$10^5[O_2]$ (mol dm^{-3})	2·42	2·56	5·01	2·27

Show that these results are in accord with the above mechanism and calculate the values of the rate constant of reaction (1) and the ratio of the rate constants of reactions (3) and (4) at 294 K.

Source: Kapralova, G. A., Buben, S. N. and Chaikin, A. M. (1975) *Kinetics and Catalysis* (English translation of *Kinetika i Kataliz*), **16**, p. 508. (U.S.S.R.)

Problem 29

Dimethyl peroxide vapour (DMP) has been thermally decomposed in a static constant volume reactor over the temperature range 396–426 K, in the presence of varying partial pressures of carbon monoxide (P_{CO}). The kinetic data indicated that at low P_{CO}, the rate of formation of CO_2 was equal to $k(0)[CO][DMP]^{1/2}$ and at high P_{CO}, the rate of formation of CO_2 was equal to $k(\infty)[DMP]$ and independent of P_{CO}, where $k(0)$ and $k(\infty)$ depend only on temperature.

Apply the steady state approximation (**10**) to show that these observations are consistent with the mechanism consisting of the elementary steps

$$CH_3OOCH_3\ (DMP) \rightarrow 2CH_3O\cdot \quad (1)$$

$$CH_3O\cdot + CO \rightarrow CO_2 + CH_3\cdot \quad (2)$$

$$CH_3O\cdot + CH_3O\cdot \rightarrow CH_3OH + CH_2O \quad (3)$$

$$CH_3O\cdot + CH_2O \rightarrow CH_3OH + HCO\cdot \quad (4)$$

$$CH_3O\cdot + HCO\cdot \rightarrow CH_3OH + CO \quad (5)$$

$$CH_3\cdot + CH_3\cdot \rightarrow C_2H_6 \quad (6)$$

$$CH_3O\cdot + CH_3\cdot \rightarrow CH_3OCH_3 \quad (7)$$

It may be assumed that formaldehyde (CH_2O) is a steady state intermediate.

The variation of $k(0)$ with temperature corresponded to an Arrhenius activation energy (E_a) of 126·8 kJ mol^{-1}, while that of $k(\infty)$ corresponded to E_a = 154·4 kJ mol^{-1} (**15**). Assuming that inter-radical reactions have rate constants with insignificant temperature coefficients, obtain estimates for:

(*a*) The bond strength of the O—O bond in DMP.

(*b*) The apparent activation energy of step (2).

Source: Lissi, E. A., Massiff, G. and Villa, A. E. (1973) *Journal of the Chemical Society, Faraday Transactions I*, **69**, p. 346. (Chile)

Problem 30

A gas-phase, flow tube system was established in which very small concentrations of ground electronic state oxygen atoms and ethylene (C_2H_4) in nitrogen carrier were rapidly mixed (**6**). The resultant elementary reactions were known to be the two steps

$$O + C_2H_4 \xrightarrow{k_1} HCO\cdot + CH_3\cdot$$

$$O + HCO\cdot \xrightarrow{k_2} \text{products}$$

and it was known that k_2 was very much greater than k_1.

When the linear velocity of the gases was 18·4 m s^{-1} at a temperature of 297 K, the gases were sampled at a series of distances (l) downstream from the point of mixing and, using a photoionisation mass spectrometer, a signal (S) at mass to charge ratio of 29, directly proportional to [HCO·], was measured. For an experiment where [O] = $3{\cdot}85 \times 10^{-9}$ mol dm^{-3}, effectively invariant with l in the range concerned, and with [C_2H_4]/[O] = 7·6, the following set of results was obtained:

S (arbitrary units)	4·54	6·19	8·10	11·34	14·52	17·54	20·75	20·75
l (mm)		9·4	13·4	18·8	30·0	45·6	70·8	368	450

It was established that HCO· was not generated by subsequent reactions of CH_3·.

Use these data to calculate the value of the rate constant k_2 (**11**) and show that it approximates to the collision frequency (**20**) of O + HCO· on a hard sphere basis with a collision diameter of 0·3 nm.

Source: Washida, N., Martinez, R. I. and Bayes, K. D. (1974) *Zeitschrift fur Naturforschung*, **29A**, p. 251. (U.S.A.)

Problem 31

The reaction of bromine, dissolved in aqueous solution containing a large excess of bromide ion, with aqueous HCN yields BrCN and HBr with unity stoichiometry. The rate has been followed using the absorbance (A) (**8**) due to Br_3^- at a wavelength of 265 nm across an optical cell maintained at a temperature of 298 K. When the initial concentrations of HCN and bromine (present as Br_2(aq) + Br_3^-) were both $1{\cdot}77 \times 10^{-4}$ mol dm^{-3}, [Br^-] = $1{\cdot}16 \times 10^{-2}$ mol dm^{-3} and [H^+] = 0·180 mol dm^{-3}, A varied with time (t) as follows:

A	1·13	0·956	0·828	0·653	0·460
t (s)	0	10	20	40	80

(*a*) Show that the decay of A corresponds to a reaction first order (**2**) in both total bromine and HCN and evaluate the apparent second order rate constant.

(*b*) With variation of the excess [Br^-] and [H^+], the apparent second order rate constant, $_2k$, varied as follows:

$_2k$ (dm^3 mol^{-1} s^{-1})	93·5	114	146	205
10^3[Br^-] (mol dm^{-3})	19·3	3·86	3·86	3·86
[H^+] (mol dm^{-3})	0·180	0·180	0·090	0·045

On the basis that pre-equilibria (**12**) are maintained corresponding to the equilibrium constants

$$K_1 = \frac{[Br_3^-]}{[Br^-][Br_2]} = 15{\cdot}2 \text{ dm}^3 \text{ mol}^{-1}$$

$$K_2 = \frac{[H^+][CN^-]}{[HCN]} = 8{\cdot}14 \times 10^{-10} \text{ mol dm}^{-3},$$

elucidate the effective elementary reactions and evaluate their rate constants.

Source: Nolan, M. F., Pendlebury, J. N. and Smith, R. H. (1975) *International Journal of Chemical Kinetics*, **7**, p. 205. (Australia)

Problem 32

The reaction between excess pyridine (Py) and sodium triphenide (Na^+Tr^-) in the presence of excess triphenylene (Tr) in tetrahydrofuran solution has been studied by the stopped flow technique. The progress of the reaction was followed using the absorbance (A) (**8**) of Tr^- at a wavelength of 672 nm. The end-products of the reaction are the dimeric anion (Py^-–Py^-) and Tr. A plot of A^{-1} versus time was linear and the slope of the plot (**2**) gave an apparent second order rate constant, ${}_2k$, which varied with concentrations as follows:

10^2[Py] (mol dm^{-3})	0·98	4·1	16·7	0·98	0·98
10^2[Tr] (mol dm^{-3})	1·1	1·1	1·1	0·20	0·55
${}_2k$ (dm^3 mol^{-1} s^{-1})	$9·0 \times 10^3$	$1·6 \times 10^5$	$2·6 \times 10^6$	$2·7 \times 10^5$	$3·6 \times 10^4$

Devise a simple mechanism for the reaction, involving a pre-equilibrium (**12**), to explain these data.

Source: Rainis, A. and Szwarc, M. (1975) *Journal of Physical Chemistry*, **79**, p. 106. (U.S.A.)

Problem 33

The oxidation of Cr^{2+} ions by nitrate ions in aqueous nitric acid solutions of constant ionic strength obeyed the pseudo-first order rate law

$$-\frac{d[Cr^{2+}]}{dt} = k_{obs}[Cr^{2+}]$$

The effective rate constant, k_{obs}, showed the following variation as a function of total added nitrate ion concentration, $[NO_3^-]_T$, and $[H^+]$ at 298 K:

Experiment number	1	2	3	4	5	6	7	8	9
$10^3[NO_3]_T$ (mol dm^{-3})	16·0	24·0	28·0	32·0	20·0	20·0	20·0	20·0	20·0
$10^2[H^+]$ (mol dm^{-3})	20·7	20·7	20·7	20·7	11·0	30·1	39·5	48·2	59·9
10^2k_{obs} (s^{-1})	4·67	7·00	8·17	9·34	3·12	8·43	11·0	13·4	16·5

If the nitric acid ionisation equilibrium (**12**) is always maintained with a concentration equilibrium constant of 15·4 mol dm^{-3} under these conditions, use the above data to show that the overwhelming initial and rate-determining step is represented by the equation

$$Cr^{2+} + HNO_3 \xrightarrow{k_1} \text{products}$$

and that the potential reaction represented as

$$Cr^{2+} + NO_3^- \rightarrow \text{products}$$

is of negligible significance. Evaluate the rate constant k_1.

Source: Ogino, H., Tsukahara, K. and Tanaka, N. (1974) *Bulletin of the Chemical Society of Japan*, **47**, p. 308. (Japan)

Problem 34

The reaction between nitrous acid (HNO_2) and iodide ions in aqueous perchloric acid medium of ionic strength 0·20 mol dm^{-3} has a mechanism based on the following elementary steps:

$$HNO_2 + H^+ \rightleftharpoons H_2NO_2^+ \quad (1)$$

$$H_2NO_2^+ + I^- \rightleftharpoons NOI + H_2O \quad (2)$$

$$NOI + I^- \rightarrow NO + I_2^- \quad (3)$$

$$I_2^- + H_2NO_2^+ \rightarrow NO + I_2 + H_2O \quad (4)$$

$$HNO_2 + HNO_2 \rightleftharpoons N_2O_3 + H_2O \quad (5)$$

$$N_2O_3 + 2H^+ \rightleftharpoons H_2N_2O_3^{2+} \quad (6)$$

$$H_2N_2O_3^{2+} + I^- \rightleftharpoons H_2N_2O_3I^+ \quad (7)$$

$$H_2N_2O_3I^+ + I^- \rightarrow 2NO + I_2 + H_2O \quad (8)$$

It is known that $k_4 \gg k_3$ and the steps represent fully-maintained equilibria or irreversible forward-going processes as indicated **(10)** **(12)**.

If $R = d[I_2]/dt$, which of the following plots would be expected to be linear on the basis of the above mechanism?

(i) R versus $[I^-]$, at constant $[H^+]$ and $[HNO_2]$,
(ii) R versus $[I^-]^2$, at constant $[H^+]$ and $[HNO_2]$,
(iii) $R/[NO_2^-]_T$ versus $[NO_2^-]_T$ at constant $[H^+]$ and $[I^-]$,
(iv) $R/[H^+]$ versus $[H^+]$ at constant $[I^-]$ and $[NO_2^-]_T$,

where $[NO_2^-]_T$ is the total nitrite originally added and HNO_2 is to be considered as a weak acid.

Source: Dosza, L., Szilassy, I. and Beck, M. T., (1976) *Inorganica Chimica Acta*, **17**, p. 147. (Hungary)

Problem 35

The homogeneous Schmidt reaction between benzoic acid and hydrazoic acid in 90–98% sulphuric acid solution at 298 K can be represented as:

$$C_6H_5COOH + HN_3 + H^+ \rightarrow C_6H_5NH_3^+ + CO_2 + N_2$$

With the reactants present in low enough concentrations to make $[H^+]$ effectively constant throughout each experiment, the experimental rate law (when $[H^+]$ was varied in different experiments) was found to be

$$-\frac{d[C_6H_5COOH]}{dt} = (\alpha + \beta[H^+])C_{C_6H_5COOH}C_{HN_3}$$

where C_X is the total concentration (including all protonated forms) of X and α and β are positive constants. From pK values it is known that the reactants exist overwhelmingly in the mono-protonated forms $C_6H_5C^+(OH)_2$ and $H_2N_3^+$ in these solutions.

On the assumption that all protonation/deprotonation pre-equilibria **(12)** are maintained, which one of the following must be regarded as an essential rate-determining step?

$$C_6H_5C^+(OH)_2 + H_2N_3^+ \rightarrow \text{products} \quad (1)$$

$$C_6H_5C(OH)_2H^{2+} + HN_3 \rightarrow \text{products} \quad (2)$$

$$C_6H_5C(OH)_2H^{2+} + H_2N_3^+ \rightarrow \text{products} \quad (3)$$

Source: Prado, J. N. A. and Bak, T. A. (1969) *Acta Chemica Scandanavica*, **23**, p. 2904. (Peru)

Problem 36

The thermal decomposition of pure dimethylsulphoxide (CH_3—S—O—CH_3) vapour has been studied at temperatures of ~600 K and pressures of ~30 kPa. In the initial stages the major products were methane, sulphur dioxide and ethylene, formed in constant relative yields. When mixtures of CH_3SOCH_3 and CD_3SOCD_3 were decomposed, the methane showed considerable isotopic scrambling (**13**) while the ethylene species C_2H_4, C_2D_4 and CH_2CD_2 appeared. It was noted that some solid sulphur was deposited on the walls of the vessel.

What mechanistic conclusions can be drawn from these observations and what is the reaction order for the formation of methane on the basis of the simplest feasible mechanism (**14**)?

Source: Thyrion, F. C. and Debrecker, G. (1973) *International Journal of Chemical Kinetics*, **5**, p. 583. (Algeria)

Problem 37

The thermal decomposition of tertiarybutyl peroxide (Bu_2O_2) in solution in 3,4-dichlorobenzyl methyl ether ($ArCH_2OMe$) showed accurate first order kinetics at a temperature of 393 K. On the basis of the elementary reaction steps

$$Bu_2O_2 \rightarrow 2BuO\cdot \tag{1}$$

$$BuO\cdot + ArCH_2OMe \rightarrow BuOH + Ar\dot{C}HOMe \tag{2}$$

$$Ar\dot{C}HOMe + Bu_2O_2 \rightarrow ArCH(OMe)OBu + BuO\cdot \tag{3}$$

$$2Ar\dot{C}HOMe \rightarrow (ArCHOMe)_2 \tag{4}$$

$$Ar\dot{C}HOMe + BuO\cdot \rightarrow ArCH(OMe)OBu \tag{5}$$

distinguish which of the two termination steps (4) and (5) dominates under these conditions (**14**).

Source: Goh, S. H. and Ong, S. H. (1970) *Journal of the Chemical Society*, **B**, p. 870. (Malaysia)

Problem 38

Sulphur dioxide in the air becomes oxidised to sulphate aerosol—one important mechanism involves solution into aqueous droplets as sulphite and subsequent reaction with dissolved metal ions.

A study has been made of the rate of the oxidation of sulphite ions, added as the sodium salt at a concentration $[SO_3^{2-}] = 1{\cdot}00 \times 10^{-5}$ mol dm^{-3} in a solution of $(NH_4)_2SO_4$ (0·1 mol dm^{-3}) containing $1{\cdot}00 \times 10^{-6}$ mol dm^{-3} of Fe^{3+} ions. The apparent order (n) of the reaction was defined by the equation

$$-\frac{d[SO_3^{2-}]}{dt} \propto [SO_3^{2-}]^n$$

In the presence of dissolved oxygen and on adjustment of the pH of the solution with strong acid, n (**36**) was found to vary as follows:

pH	5·0	4·4	4·0	3·8
n	1·8	1·4	1·1	1·0

Show that this variation of n is consistent with the mechanism (**14**)

$$SO_3^{2-} + Fe^{3+} \rightarrow Fe^{2+} + SO_3^{-}\cdot \quad (1)$$

$$SO_3^{-}\cdot + O_2 \rightarrow SO_5^{-}\cdot \quad (2)$$

$$SO_5^{-}\cdot + SO_3^{2-} \rightarrow SO_3^{-}\cdot + SO_5^{2-} \quad (3)$$

$$SO_5^{2-} + SO_3^{2-} \rightarrow 2SO_4^{2-} \quad (4)$$

$$SO_5^{-}\cdot + T \rightarrow \text{inert products} \quad (5)$$

where T is a trace impurity present at a constant level, on the basis that the sulphurous acid/sulphite equilibrium is always maintained with pK values of 1·81 and 6·99 for the first and second hydrogens of H_2SO_3.

Calculate the ratio of the rates of reactions (3) and (5) at pH = 5·0.

(Hint: Equate apparent and actual rate laws through $d \ln (\text{rate})/d[SO_3^{2-}]$.)

Source: Brimblecombe, P. and Spedding, D. J. (1974) *Chemosphere*, **1**, p. 29. (New Zealand)

Problem 39

The second explosion limit in H_2/O_2 mixtures can be explained by the mechanism (numbering scheme of the source retained) (**16**)

$$H + O_2 \rightarrow OH + O \quad (2)$$

$$O + H_2 \rightarrow OH + H \quad (3)$$

$$OH + H_2 \rightarrow H_2O + H \quad (1)$$

$$H + O_2 + M \rightarrow HO_2 + M \quad (4)$$

where M represents any species present in the system. It is assumed that HO_2 radicals are destroyed at the (KCl-coated) vessel walls without regeneration of active species.

At a temperature of 793 K, the mol fractions ($i_{1/2}$) of tetraethylsilane ($SiEt_4$) required to halve [M] at the explosion limit compared to the uninhibited reaction for various mol fractions x (of H_2) and y (of O_2) were as follows:

Experiment number	1	2	3
$10^4 i_{1/2}$	2·78	3·42	6·89
x	0·14	0·56	0·14
y	0·14	0·14	0·56

On the basis that the inhibition arises solely from the reactions

$$H + SiEt_4 \rightarrow \text{non-propagating products} \quad (24)$$

$$OH + SiEt_4 \rightarrow \text{non-propagating products} \quad (25)$$

derive values of the ratios of rate constants k_{24}/k_2 and k_{25}/k_1 at 793 K.

(Suggestion: Derive values from experiments 1 and 2 and test in experiment 3).

Source: Baldwin, R. R., Everett, C. J. and Walker, R. W. (1968) *Transactions of the Faraday Society*, **64**, p. 2708. (U.K.)

Problem 40

Ethylene dissolved in cyclohexane has been polymerised using chromium oxide deposited on a porous, particulate silica support in suspension at temperatures in the range 313–348 K. Overall rates of polymerisation (R) were measured in terms of ethylene consumption when at a certain time the polymerisation was quenched by injection of an excess of radioactively-labelled methanol, $^{14}CH_3OH$, which is known to act by quantitatively terminating all growing chains with addition of a group containing ^{14}C. By measurement of the specific radioactivity of the resultant polymer, the number (n) of growing chains at the moment of quenching was obtained. Ethylene concentrations in the solution were held constant by maintaining the pressure of the gas over the solution. The following results were obtained using 0·001 kg of catalyst in a constant volume of solution:

Experiment number	1	2	3	4	5	6
T (K)	313	323	333	348	348	348
R ((mol C_2H_4) dm^{-3} h^{-1})	0·342	0·425	0·519	1·231	1·311	4·150
$10^6 n$ (mol)	0·30	0·30	0·30	0·54	1·15	1·82
$[C_2H_4]$ (mol dm^{-3})	0·95	0·95	0·95	0·95	0·475	0·95

Show that the chain length (**17**) can be considered as long and evaluate the apparent activation energy (**5**) of the propagation step.

Source: Zakharov, V. A. and Ermankov, Y. I. (1971) *Journal of Polymer Science*, **9**, p. 3129. (U.S.S.R.)

Problem 41

Vinyl chloride in benzene solution has been polymerised using the modified Ziegler–Natta catalyst formed by addition of vanadium oxytrichloride, tri-isobutyl aluminium and tetrahydrofuran. The rate of polymerisation (R_t) at time t was established by dilatometry.

At low conversions of monomer, values of R_t/R_o at various times after the start of reaction (R_o is the initial rate) were measured as follows:

R_t/R_o	0·851	0·741	0·656	0·588
t (min)	100	200	300	400

In the same reaction system, measurements of the unreacted monomer concentration at time t, $[M]_t$, were as follows relative to the initial concentration, $[M]_o$:

$[M]_o/[M]_t$	1·327	1·524	1·892
t (min)	1000	2000	5000

Show that these results are consistent with addition polymerisation of vinyl chloride with a mechanism where the active centres are formed immediately upon mixing the catalyst components, the chain propagation (**17**) step involves interaction of one growing active centre with one monomer molecule and termination is second order (**2**) in the active centre concentration. Evaluate the ratio of the propagation rate constant to the effective termination rate constant (k_p/k_d).

Source: Haszeldine, R. N., Hyde, T. G. and Tait, P. J. T. (1973) *Polymer*, **14**, p. 224. (U.K.)

Problem 42

Methylmethacrylate can be polymerised in aqueous solution using the bisulphite ion as the initiator of anionic addition polymerisation (**18**). When 0·010 kg of monomer in 0·10 dm^3 of water containing 0·050 mol dm^{-3} of sodium bisulphite was polymerised in the absence and presence of finely-divided ferric oxide held in suspension, the overall rates of polymerisation—$10^5 R$ (mol dm^{-3} s^{-1})—at two temperatures (T) were as follows:

Fe_2O_3 (g)	T (K)	
	313	323
0	2·1	3·4
1·5	8·6	11·8

The number-average molecular weights of the resultant polymers ($\bar{M}_N$) were determined by viscosity measurements of their solutions in benzene, after the polymerisation was stopped by addition of sodium hydroxide solution. $\bar{M}_N$ varied from $1·4 \times 10^6$ in the absence of ferric oxide to $2·8 \times 10^5$ when 1·5 g of Fe_2O_3 was present, both at 323 K. Deduce the general kinetic features of the catalysis induced by ferric oxide (**17**).

Source: Moustafa, A. B. and Abd-el-hakim, A. A. (1976) *Journal of Polymer Science* (Polymer Chemistry Edition), **14**, p. 433. (Egypt)

Problem 43

The electrolytically-initiated polymerisation of tetrahydrofuran (THF) has been carried out in bulk using small additions of tetrabutylammonium perchlorate as the electrolyte. After rapid passage of a charge of 1·23 mF, the anolyte (i.e. the contents of the anode compartment) of volume $2·0 \times 10^{-2}$ dm^3 was isolated at a temperature of 303 K: the monomer concentration, [M], and the number-average molecular weight ($\bar{M}_N$) of poly-THF were measured as a function of reaction time (t) as follows:

$10^{-4}t$ (s)	0	0·20	0·50	1·00	1·50
[M] (mol dm^{-3})	10·8	9·57	8·26	6·65	5·55
$10^{-4}\bar{M}_N$	0·0072	0·736	1·52	2·49	3·14

The final state of the system represented a monomer–polymer equilibrium, when the monomer concentration, $[M]_e$, was 3·24 mol dm^{-3}. The rate law for the formation of such a "living" polymer (**18**) is then

$$-\frac{d[M]}{dt} = k_p[P^*]([M]-[M]_e)$$

where k_p is the rate constant for propagation and [P*] is the concentration of the propagating end.

Calculate [P*] and show that the $\bar{M}_N$ values above are consistent with a "living" polymer. Calculate the value of k_p and, on the basis that P* is formed initially only by a one-electron transfer in electrolysis, evaluate the current efficiency for its formation.

(Faraday's laws of electrolysis)

Source: Nakahama, S., Hino, S. and Yamazaki, N. (1971) *Polymer Journal*, **2**, p. 56. (Japan)

Problem 44

At a temperature of 531 K, the thermal decompositions of CCl_3SiCl_3(C) and CCl_3SiF_3(F) have been used separately to generate dichlorocarbene radicals ($CCl_2\cdot$)

in the presence of cis-2-butene. The subsequent addition process formed a vibrationally-excited cis-1,l-dichloro-2,3-dimethylcyclopropane molecule (S^*), which was either stabilised collisionally to yield S or decomposed to yield products, collectively referred to as D. The variation of the [D]/[S] ratio was studied as a function of total pressure (P) with cis-2-butene present in large excess. The results were as follows:

10^2[D]/[S]	16·9	7·31	5·21	3·51	21·0	11·7	7·83	5·50
P (kPa)	1·66	3·83	5·37	7·98	2·36	4·25	6·33	9·01
Source	C	C	C	C	F	F	F	F

Show that these results can be interpreted in terms of competition between decomposition of S^* with an average first order rate constant $\langle k(E)\rangle$ **(20)** over the energy (E) range produced and de-energisation of S^* at every collision with cis-2-butene. If the collision diameter in the latter process is 0·74 nm, evaluate $\langle k(E)\rangle$ for the two sources. How might the difference be accounted for in general terms?

Source: Heydtmann, H., Bardorff, W. and Rullmann, H. (1976) *Berichte Bunsen-gesellschaft fur Physikalische Chemie*, **80**, p. 311. (West Germany)

Problem 45

The rates of change of pressure and formation of nitrogen in slowly-reacting mixtures of $H_2+O_2+He+N_2O$ in a closed vessel at a temperature of 773 K have been measured. Plots of the partial pressure of N_2 (P_{N_2}) versus the total pressure change (ΔP) were found to be linear with gradients (G) as a function of the initial partial pressures given below (same P):

Experiment number	P_{H2}	P_{O_2} (kPa)	P_{N_2O}	P_{He}	G
1	18·6	9·4	6·7	31·9	0·0435
2	18·6	4·7	6·7	36·6	0·0880
3	4·7	9·4	6·7	45·9	0·0555
4	18·6	9·4	3·4	35·2	0·0245

On the basis of the mechanism **(16)**

$$OH+H_2 \rightarrow H_2O+H \quad (1)$$
$$H+O_2 \rightarrow OH+O \quad (2)$$
$$O+H_2 \rightarrow OH+H \quad (3)$$
$$H+O_2+M \rightarrow HO_2+M \quad (4)$$
$$H+N_2O \rightarrow OH+N_2 \quad (5)$$

and given that the rate constant ratio $k_2/k_4 \equiv 2{\cdot}5$ kPa for $M=H_2$ at 773 K and the relative third body (M) efficiencies **(21)** in reaction (4) are as $He:O_2:H_2:N_2O::0{\cdot}35:0{\cdot}35:1{\cdot}00:1{\cdot}50$, calculate the value of the rate constant ratio **(10)** k_5/k_2 at 773 K. (Assume that HO_2 does not propagate the chain and releases O_2 on destruction.)

Source: Baldwin, R. R., Gethin, A. and Walker, R. W. (1973) *Journal of the Chemical Society, Faraday Transactions I*, **69**, p. 352. (U.K.)

Problem 46

The termolecular combination reaction:

$$OH+NO+M \rightarrow HONO+M$$

has been studied by following [OH] decay rates absorptiometrically in the presence of NO and a large excess of inert gas, M, following ultraviolet flash photolysis of water vapour as the source of OH radicals. Apparent second order rate constants, ${}_2k$, defined by the equation

$$-\frac{d[\mathrm{OH}]}{dt} = {}_2k[\mathrm{OH}][\mathrm{NO}]$$

were measured at a temperature of 295 K for $M = H_2O$ and He in turn and the values of $10^{-8}\,{}_2k$ ($dm^3\ mol^{-1}\ s^{-1}$) at various [M] were as below:

	10^3[M] (mol dm^{-3})					
	0·192	0·427	0·854	5·30	10·9	34·5
$M = H_2O$	3·08	6·64	12·6	—	—	—
M = He	—	—	—	2·79	5·56	16·0

Show that these results accord with the energy transfer theory (**22**) of termolecular combination reactions, involving the steps

$$\mathrm{OH + NO \rightleftarrows HONO^*}$$
$$\mathrm{HONO^* + M \rightarrow HONO + M}$$

The collision diameters (**20**) of these molecules are 0·44 nm (HONO*), 0·30 nm (H_2O) and 0·26 nm (He). If H_2O deactivates HONO* at every collision, evaluate the collisional efficiency of He in deactivating HONO*.
Source: Overend, R., Paraskevopoulos, G. and Black, C. (1976) *Journal of Chemical Physics*, **64**, p. 4149. (Canada)

Problem 47
Fluorine atoms have been generated in a cylindrical silica flow tube (24·0 mm internal diameter) by upstream discharging of F_2 at large dilution in helium. Reactant inlet jets were inset along the tube at distances (l) upstream from a mass spectrometer sampling inlet (**6**). At a temperature of 298 K with a total gas flowrate of $1{\cdot}28 \times 10^{-4}$ mol s^{-1} and total pressure of 140 Pa, the addition of a flow rate (**2**) of $1{\cdot}50 \times 10^{-9}$ mol s^{-1} of Br_2 at the jets in turn produced the following mass spectrometer signals (S) proportional to [Br_2] as a function of l for the jet used:

S (arbitrary units)	81·4	69·0	45·4	32·0
l (mm)	35	65	135	195

A gas titration procedure was used to show that the flowrate of Br_2 which was equivalent to that of the F atoms was $4{\cdot}80 \times 10^{-8}$ mol s^{-1}.
Verify the statement that these results are indicative of the reaction:

$$\mathrm{F + Br_2 \rightarrow BrF + Br}$$

occurring at close to the hard sphere collision rate (**23**): the collision diameters are to be taken as 0·25 and 0·35 nm respectively for F atoms and Br_2 molecules respectively.
Source: Appleman, E. H. and Clyne, M. A. A. (1975) *Journal of the Chemical Society, Faraday Transactions I*, **71**, p. 2072. (U.K.)

Problem 48
The photolysis of DBr or DI (DX) with ultraviolet radiation has been used to generate "hot" D atoms (D*) with well-defined kinetic energies in the presence of ethane, at

ambient temperature. The mechanism following the primary photodissociation can be represented as

$$D^* + C_2H_6 \rightarrow HD + C_2H_5 \quad (1)$$

$$D^* + DX \rightarrow D_2 + X \quad (2)$$

$$D^* + DX \rightarrow D + DX \quad (3)$$

$$D^* + C_2H_6 \rightarrow D + C_2H_6 \quad (4)$$

where D is a thermalised atom which yields D_2 by subsequent reaction with DX. The ratio of yields $[D_2]/[HD]$ was plotted against $[DX]/[C_2H_6]$ for a particular kinetic energy (E) of D* and yielded linear plots with positive intercepts (I) as listed below (no HD was detected for $E = 39{\cdot}56$ kJ mol^{-1}):

E (kJ mol^{-1})	56·93	81·05	102·3	155·4	188·2	270·2
I	29·3	7·06	4·29	2·54	2·34	2·16

Use these data to estimate the value of the rate constant at a temperature of 2500 K for the reaction of thermalised (**23**) D atoms with ethane:

$$D + C_2H_6 \rightarrow HD + C_2H_5$$

on the assumption that relative kinetic energy in two dimensions alone drives the reaction. The relevant collision cross-section may be taken as 0·4 nm^2. Compare your result with the experimental value of 4×10^{10} dm^3 mol^{-1} s^{-1}.

Source: Nicholas, J. E., Bayrakceken, F. and Fink, R. D. (1972) *Journal of Chemical Physics*, **56**, p. 1008. (U.S.A.)

Problem 49

When the ion $Co(NH_3)_5NO_2^{2+}$ in solution was irradiated with light of wavelength 365 nm, the products corresponding to the two processes

$$Co(NH_3)_5NO_2^{2+} + h\nu \nearrow Co(NH_3)_5ONO^{2+} \quad (I)$$

$$Co(NH_3)_5NO_2^{2+} + h\nu \searrow Co^{2+} + 5NH_3 + NO_2 \quad (D)$$

representing isomerisation (I) and decomposition (D) caused by absorption of a single photon, were detected. Measurements were made of the respective quantum yields (ϕ_I and ϕ_D) (**38**) in glycerol/water solutions with viscosity coefficients η expressed relative to that of pure water. At a temperature of 293 K the variations below were found:

ϕ_D	0·279	0·240	0·204	0·179	0·150	0·116
ϕ_I	0·083	0·114	0·139	0·154	0·178	0·208
η	1·11	2·65	5·29	8·23	15·5	36·0

Assuming that the initial photochemical act is the formation of a geminate pair, respresented as $[Co(NH_3)_5^{2+} \cdot NO_2]$ in a solvent cage, that the effective rate constant for diffusion apart of the two species is proportional to $\eta^{-1/2}$ and that $Co(NH_3)_5^{2+}$ fragments to $Co^{2+} + 5NH_3$ immediately after escape from the solvent cage, interpret these results quantitatively, evaluating the fraction of geminate pairs (**24**) which would revert to the original ion rather than isomerise in a solvent of limiting high viscosity.

Source: Scandola, F., Bartocci, C. and Scandola, M. A. (1973) *Journal of the American Chemical Society*, **95**, p. 7898. (Italy)

Problem 50

When azoisobutyronitrile (AIBN) is used as a thermal initiator for free radical polymerisation in solution, a substantial fraction of the primary (2-cyano-2-propyl) radicals (2 per AIBN decomposed) do not initiate polymerisation **(17)** but interact within the solvent cage by combination or disproportionation, the latter yielding isobutyronitrile and methylacrylonitrile (MAN).

Radioactive-labelled **(13)** (^{14}C) AIBN has been used to initiate polymerisation of non-radioactive MAN in dimethylsulphoxide solution and the specific radioactivity of recovered MAN (S_M) and the specific radioactivity of the separated poly-MAN (S_P) have been measured after a reaction time (t). The value of S for the (^{14}C) AIBN was $1{\cdot}56 \times 10^{10}$ d. min^{-1} mol^{-1} and the following results were obtained in experiments conducted at 333 K:

$[MAN]_o$ (mol dm^{-3})	5·67	5·76	5·69	5·68
$10^3[AIBN]_o$ (mol dm^{-3})	8·98	9·03	8·97	8·91
t (min)	300	602	900	1199
$10^{-5}S_M$ (d. min^{-1} mol^{-1})	1·08	2·00	2·82	3·50
$10^{-7}S_P$ (d. min^{-1} mol^{-1})	3·59	3·33	3·09	2·92
Polymerisation (%)	6·53	12·7	18·7	23·8

(S_P refers to per mol of MAN units in the polymer and subscript 0 indicates initial concentrations).

On the assumption that (^{14}C) MAN formed by geminate disproportionation was diluted with non-radioactive MAN the moment it diffused out of the cage **(24)** and given a rate constant of $1{\cdot}20 \times 10^{-5}$ s^{-1} for AIBN decomposition at 333 K, calculate the fractions of AIBN available for geminate (i.e. in cage) reactions and for geminate disproportionation.

(Isotopic dilution analysis)

Source: Ayrey, G., Evans, K. L. and Wong, D. J. D. (1973) *European Polymer Journal*, **9**, p. 1347. (U.K.)

Problem 51

When $6{\cdot}0 \times 10^{-5}$ mol dm^{-3} HgI_2 aqueous solutions have been flash photolysed with 265 nm radiation (30 ns flash duration), the primary process is represented:

$$HgI_2 + h\nu \rightarrow I + HgI$$

HgI absorbs radiation at 380 nm wavelength and in the absence of I^- it decays so that at time t the optical density of the solution is A_1 **(8)** When I^- was present, I_2^- is formed in the solution and this also absorbs radiation at 380 nm, so that the total optical density of the solution at time t is A_2. $\Delta A = A_2 - A_1$ is considered to be the optical density due to I_2^- absorption only; at longer reaction times this parameter reaches a limiting value, ΔA_{max}.

At a temperature of 298 K, the following values of $\Delta A/\Delta A_{max}$ were found as a function of reaction time t and $[I^-]$:

$10^5[I^-]$ (mol dm^{-3})	$10^6 t$ (s)					
	0·15	0·24	0·37	0·51	0·67	0·84
2·0	0·248	0·366	0·505	0·621	0·720	0·797
3·8	0·268	0·393	0·537	0·654	0·752	0·826
7·7	0·310	0·447	0·599	0·716	0·809	0·874

Show that these results are consistent with the elementary steps

$$I^- + I \xrightarrow{k_1} I_2^- \quad (1)$$

$$I_2^- \xrightarrow{k_{-1}} I + I^- \quad (-1)$$

and evaluate k_1 and k_{-1}, assuming that $[I] \ll [I^-]$ (**7**).

By calculating the diffusion-limiting rate constant (**25**) assuming that reaction takes place at every encounter for recombination of I atoms in aqueous solution, show that this process cannot compete significantly with reaction (1) under these conditions. The coefficient of viscosity of water at 298 K is $8{\cdot}937 \times 10^{-3}$ P.

Source: Fournier de Violet, P., Bonneau, R. and Logan, S. R. (1974) *Journal of Physical Chemistry*, **78**, p. 1698. (France)

Problem 52

A microwave-pulse temperature jump technique has been used to study the proton-transfer complex formation between 2,4-dinitrophenol (DNP) and tri-n-butylamine (TNB) in a series of solvents. For added concentrations of $[DNP] = 3{\cdot}90 \times 10^{-5}$ mol dm^{-3} and $[TNB] = 5{\cdot}80 \times 10^{-5}$ mol dm^{-3}, the concentration equilibrium constants (K) were established from the absorbance of the complex at 400 nm wavelength and characteristic relaxation times (τ) (**8**) were measured for solutions at a temperature of 295 K with solvent visosity coefficients (η) as follows:

Solvent	n-butyl chloride	chlorobenzene	iodobenzene
K ($dm^3\ mol^{-1}$)	5850	4500	5700
τ (μs)	6·76	8·73	18·8
$10^4\eta$ ($kg\ m^{-1}\ s^{-1}$)	4·40	7·78	15·9

Evaluate the second order rate constants for complex formation and show that these vary with η as expected for a diffusion-limited reaction (**25**).

Source: Ivin, K. J., McGarvey, J. J., Simmons, E. L. and Small, R. (1971) *Transactions of the Faraday Society*, **67**, p. 104. (U.K.)

Problem 53

The thermal decomposition of methyl chloroformate vapour in the presence of substantial amounts of propylene to inhibit chain reactions proceeds as:

$$ClCOOCH_3 \rightarrow CH_3Cl + CO_2$$

In a static constant volume reactor at a temperature of 733·4 K, the following total pressure (P) readings were taken as a function of time (t) when the initial partial pressure of $ClCOOCH_3$ was 11·57 kPa (**26**):

P (kPa)	27·53	27·81	28·21	28·83	30·43	32·11	33·33
t (s)	0	100	250	500	1200	2100	2900

Evaluate the first order rate constant for $ClCOOCH_3$ decomposition at 733·4 K.

Other values of the rate constant (${}_1k$) for the reaction were as follows for different temperatures (T):

T (K)	698·8	712·5	721·7	753·0
$10^4\,{}_1k$ (s^{-1})	0·30	0·68	1·25	7·09

Evaluate the Arrhenius pre-exponential factor and the entropy of activation of this reaction, commenting on the result.
Source: Johnston, R. L. and Stimson, V. R. (1977) *Australian Journal of Chemistry*, **30**, p. 1917. (Australia)

Problem 54
The thermal unimolecular decomposition of N-allylcyclo-hexylamine (ACA) vapour yields cyclohexylamine and propylene as the sole products:

ACA

The first-order rate constant (${}_1k$) was independent of initial pressure **(19)** in the range of 2–20 kPa used and also of the surface to volume ratio **(6)** of the Pyrex reaction vessel. At a series of temperatures (T), ${}_1k$ varied as follows:

$10^4\,{}_1k\,(s^{-1})$	0·1091	0·3104	0·8864	4·171	20·05
T (K)	562	578	595	622	652

Use these data and the bond dissociation energy values below to discuss the nature of the transition state involved in this decomposition **(26)**.

$$D(\text{allyl-NH}) = 304\ \text{kJ mol}^{-1}$$
$$D(H{-}C_6H_{10}) = 397\ \text{kJ mol}^{-1}$$
$$D(C_6H_{10}{=}NH) = 285\ \text{kJ mol}^{-1} + \text{energy of } \sigma \text{ bond}$$
$$D(H{-}(C{=}C)) = 452\ \text{kJ mol}^{-1}$$

Source: Egger, K. W. (1973) *Journal of the Chemical Society, Perkin Transactions 2*, p. 2007. (Switzerland)

Problem 55
The homogeneous, elementary gas phase reaction of thioacetic acid and ketene to form acetic thioanhydride is reversible and is represented as

$$CH_3COSH + CH_2CO \rightleftarrows (CH_3CO)_2S$$

The initial rates of the forward (f) and reverse (b) reactions have been measured separately, yielding the rate constants (k) below at temperatures (T):

$k_f\,(dm^3\,mol^{-1}\,s^{-1})$	3·26	5·04	8·51	15·1			
$10^4 k_b (s^{-1})$				1·74	8·14	23·0	102
T (K)	401·0	417·0	438·0	463·0	485·0	501·0	526·0

Equilibrium constants were measured in the same temperature range from the final composition of the reacted mixtures and these yielded parameters for the overall reaction, $\Delta H^\circ = -95 \pm 2\ \text{kJ mol}^{-1}$ and $\Delta S^\circ = -140 \pm 10\ \text{J mol}^{-1}\,\text{K}^{-1}$, both referred to a standard state of $1{\cdot}013 \times 10^5$ Pa.

Calculate $\Delta H^\ddagger$ and $\Delta S^\ddagger$ parameters **(26)** for both reactions and show that in

combination they accord with the statement of the Principle of Microscopic Reversibility (7) that forward and reverse reactions follow the same detailed enthalpy and entropy pathways in opposite directions.
(N.B. The standard state for the kinetic measurements is 1 mol cm^{-3}).
Source: Blake, P. G. and Speis, A. (1974) *Journal of the Chemical Society, Perkin Transactions 2*, p. 1879. (U.K.)

Problem 56

The thermal isomerisation of cyclopropane (CP) vapour into propylene is homogeneously catalysed by boron trichloride vapour or HBr gas. The reactions are entirely homogeneous and bimolecular. The second order rate constants ($_2k$) varied with temperature (T) as follows:

T (K)		650·0	685·0	715·0	740·0
$_2k$ ($dm^3\ mol^{-1}\ s^{-1}$)	(BCl_3)	0·624	1·709	3·747	6·868
	(HBr)	0·0272	0·126	0·417	1·048

Evaluate the Arrhenius parameters for each reaction and hence the enthalpies and entropies of activation (**26**). Comment on the differences in terms of the general nature of the transition states involved.
Source: Johnson, R. J., and Stimson, V. R. (1975) *Australian Journal of Chemistry*, **28**, p. 447. (Australia)

Problem 57

The Diels–Alder cyclo-addition reaction between 2,3-dimethylbutadiene (B) and dimethyl fumarate (F) has been carried out in n-butyl chloride solution at a temperature of 313 K. The reaction is known to be bimolecular and its kinetics are insensitive to solvent change (polar to non-polar).

For initial concentrations of $[B]_o = 0{\cdot}113$ mol dm^{-3} and $[F]_o = 0{\cdot}190$ mol dm^{-3}, it was found that plots of ln ([F]/[B]) versus time were linear (**2**) with gradients (G) which varied as a function of the applied pressure (P_r), expressed as a ratio to $1{\cdot}013 \times 10^5$ Pa, as follows:

10^7G (s^{-1})	5·08	9·63	16·1
P_r	1·0	500	900

Calculate the volume of activation (**27**) of this reaction. Consider the significance of the result compared to the partial molar volume change of $-3{\cdot}72 \times 10^{-5}$ m^3 mol^{-1} from reactants to the product.
Source: Seguchi, K., Sera, A. and Maruyama, K. (1974) *Bulletin of the Chemical Society of Japan*, **47**, p. 2242. (Japan)

Problem 58

The complex formed by haem (Hm) and carbon monoxide in glycol/water (80% v/v) solutions is partially-photodissociated on subjecting the solution to a ruby-laser pulse at a wavelength of 694 nm. The optical absorption of Hm at a wavelength of 430 nm has been used to follow [Hm] as a function of time (t) following the pulse. In a solution where the initial addition of Hm corresponded to a concentration of $9{\cdot}20 \times 10^{-6}$ mol

dm^{-3} and the initial addition of CO corresponded to a concentration of $1{\cdot}53 \times 10^{-5}$ mol dm^{-3}, the results for an applied pressure of $1{\cdot}0 \times 10^{5}$ Pa were as follows:

10^7[Hm] (mol dm^{-3})	6·40	5·30	4·39	3·64	3·02	2·50
t (ms)	0	1·0	2·0	3·0	4·0	5·0

(*a*) Show that these results are consistent with a very large value for the complex-formation equilibrium constant (K=[HmCO]/[Hm][CO]) and evaluate the rate constant (k_f) (**2**) for the recombination process:

$$\text{Hm} + \text{CO} \rightarrow \text{HmCO}$$

(*b*) When the applied pressure (P) was varied at a temperature of 293 K, a plot of ln k_f versus P was found to be linear with a gradient of $-8{\cdot}42 \times 10^{-10}$ Pa^{-1}. Evaluate the volume of activation (**27**) for this recombination. How may the sign of this parameter be interpreted?
Source: Caldin, E. F. and Hasinoff, B. B. (1975) *Journal of the Chemical Society, Faraday Transactions I*, **71**, p. 515. (U.K.)

Problem 59
Temperature jump experiments on the equilibrium between Ni^{2+} ions and murexide ions (Mu^-) represented as

$$Ni^{2+} + Mu^- \underset{k_b}{\overset{k_f}{\rightleftharpoons}} NiMu^+$$

have yielded the following characteristic relaxation times, τ (ms) (**8**), as a function of applied pressure (P) and the initially-added concentration of Ni^{2+} ($[Ni^{2+}]_o$) when the initially-added concentration of Mu^- was always $5{\cdot}0 \times 10^{-5}$ mol dm^{-3} and the relaxation took place at a temperature of 298 K. The ionic strength of the solution was maintained at 0·1 mol dm^{-3} using $NaClO_4$ which was inert chemically.

$10^3[Ni^{2+}]_o$ (mol dm^{-3})	P (bars) 1·00	800	1500
0·80	75·2	77·5	74·4
2·00	39·5	47·4	52·0
6·00	15·3	20·7	26·0

Calculate the volume of activation (**27**) and the partial molar volume change for formation of the complex ion. How may these values be interpreted?
Source: Jost, A. (1975) *Berichte Bunsengesellschaft fur Physikalische Chemie*, **79**, p. 850. (West Germany)

Problem 60
The oxidation of plutonium(III) ions by persulphate ions proceeds according to the stoichiometric equation:

$$2\,Pu^{3+} + S_2O_8^{2-} \rightarrow 2\,Pu^{4+} + 2SO_4^{2-}$$

In aqueous perchloric acid solutions (2·5 mol dm^{-3}) of constant ionic strength (2·6 mol dm^{-3}), a second order rate law was found to hold:

$$-\frac{d[Pu^{3+}]}{dt} = {}_2k[Pu^{3+}][S_2O_8^{2-}]$$

and the rate constant ${}_2k$ varied with temperature (T) as follows:

$10^{-3}\,{}_2k$ (dm^3 mol^{-1} s^{-1})	0·241	0·497	1·05	2·08
T (K)	304·0	314·0	324·0	334·0

On the basis of the mechanism

$$Pu^{3+} + S_2O_8^{2-} \rightarrow Pu^{4+} + SO_4^{2-} + SO_4^{-} \quad (1)$$
$$Pu^{3+} + SO_4^{-} \rightarrow Pu^{4+} + SO_4^{2-} \quad (2)$$

with step (1) rate-determining, evaluate the enthalpy and entropy of activation (**29**) for reaction (1) and interpret the sign of the latter.
Source: Shilov, V. P., Milovanov, A. I. and Krot, N. N., (1974) *Soviet Radiochemistry* (English translation of *Radiokhymia*), **16**, p. 197. (U.S.S.R.)

Problem 61
The reaction of heptamolybdate ion ($Mo_7O_{24}^{6-}$) with excess hydroxide ion:

$$Mo_7O_{24}^{6-} + 8OH^- \rightarrow 7MoO_4^{2-} + 4H_2O$$

involves a base-dependent pathway where the rate is defined as:

$$-\frac{d[Mo_7O_{24}^{6-}]}{dt} = k_{obs}[Mo_7O_{24}^{6-}][OH^-]$$

The observed rate constant, k_{obs}, in solutions of ionic strength of 2·0 mol dm^{-3} maintained with NaCl, has the following values as a function of temperature (T):

$10^{-3}\,k_{obs}$ (dm^3 mol^{-1} s^{-1})	5·36	7·99	11·8	17·1
T (K)	288·0	293·0	298·0	303·0

Calculate the entropy of activation (**29**) for this reaction and hence decide between the two possible rate-determining components of the mechanism below:

mechanism A

$$Mo_7O_{24}^{6-} + OH^- \rightarrow \text{products}$$

mechanism B

$$Mo_7O_{24}^{6-} + OH^- \rightleftharpoons Mo_7O_{24}OH^{7-}$$
$$Mo_7O_{24}OH^{7-} \rightarrow \text{products}$$

Source: Druskovich, D. M. and Kepert, D. L. (1975) *Australian Journal of Chemistry*, **28**, p. 2365. (Australia)

Problem 62
The rate of reaction between octacyanomolybdate(V) ions ($Mo(CN)_8^{3-}$) and iodide ions in aqueous solution at a temperature of 303 K has been determined spectrophotometrically by measurement of the rate of appearance of the product I_3^- absorption. The overall reaction has the stoichiometry represented by

$$2\,Mo(CN)_8^{3-} + 3I^- \rightarrow 2Mo(CN)_8^{4-} + I_3^-$$

Under the conditions specified below, the reaction showed first order kinetics, yielding the values below of an apparent rate constant, ${}_1k$, defined by

$$-\frac{d[Mo(CN)_8^{3-}]}{dt} = {}_1k[Mo(CN)_8^{3-}]$$

Each solution had an initial concentration of $5{\cdot}0 \times 10^{-5}$ mol dm^{-3} with varying ionic strength (I) produced using sodium perchlorate as the inert salt.

$10^4[I^-]$ (mol dm^{-3})	10·0	25·0	50·0	10·0	10·0	10·0
$10^3 I$ (mol dm^{-3})	10	10	10	1·6	4·5	8·6
$10^3\,{}_1k$ (s^{-1})	1·38	3·44	6·88	0·901	1·09	1·31

Use these results to indicate a bimolecular rate-determining step

$$Mo(CN)_8^{3-} + I^- \rightarrow \text{products}$$

on the basis of the Debye–Huckel limiting law for the activity coefficient (γ_A) (**30**) of an A ion with charge Z_A, expressed for the above conditions as

$$\log_{10} \gamma_A = -0{\cdot}51 Z_A^2 I^{1/2}$$

Source: Ford-Smith, H. M. and Rawsthorne, J. H. (1969) *Journal of the Chemical Society*, A, p. 160. (U.K.)

Problem 63

The aquation reaction of the tris(malonate) cobaltate(III) ion ($Co(mal)_3^{3-}$) to $Co(H_2O)_6^{3+}$ has been studied in 0·01–0·30 mol dm^{-3} perchloric acid solution with ionic strengths (I) adjusted in the range 0·10–1·00 mol dm^{-3} using sodium perchlorate. The optical absorption of $Co(mal)_3^{3-}$ at a wavelength of 610 nm was followed as a function of time; the decay was first order in $[Co(mal)_3^{3-}]$ with rate constant k_{obs} for particular values of I and $[H^+]$. At a temperature of 298 K, the variations of k_{obs} with I and $[H^+]$ were as given in the table below—values listed are $10^2\ k_{obs}$ (s^{-1}):

$[H^+]$ (mol dm^{-3})	I (mol dm^{-3})		
	0·20	0·30	0·50
0·10	1·36	1·26	1·01
0·15	2·30	2·12	1·71
0·20	3·41	3·13	2·56
0·25	—	4·29	3·54
0·30	—	5·60	4·67

Show that these results can be interpreted on the basis of two competing elementary reactions of $Co(mal)_3^{3-}$, one first order in $[H^+]$ and the other second order in $[H^+]$ (**31**). (No quantitative treatment of salt effects required.)
Source: Sulkfab, Y. and Al-obadie, M. S. (1974) *Journal of Inorganic and Nuclear Chemistry*, **36**, p. 2067. (Kuwait)

Problem 64

A stopped-flow system using spectrophotometric measurement of MnO_4^- decay rates has yielded values of an apparent second order rate constant, ${}_2k$, for the reaction of MnO_4^- with a ten-fold excess of maleic acid, (H_2A), defined by the rate law

$$-\frac{d[MnO_4^-]}{dt} = {}_2k[MnO_4^-][H_2A]_T$$

where $[H_2A]_T$ represents the total concentration of maleic acid added. The pH of the solution could be adjusted with strong acid and the ionic strength (I) with non-common ion salts. At a temperature of 298 K, with $[H_2A]_T = 0{\cdot}010$ mol dm^{-3}, the following results were obtained:

$10^{-2}{}_2k$ (dm^3 mol^{-1} s^{-1})	10·6	10·6	10·2	14·2	12·9	18·5	16·0	14·1	12·0
I (mol dm^{-3})	3·0	1·5	0·37	1·5	0·10	1·5	1·5	1·5	1·5
pH	0·22	0·22	1·35	1·35	2·95	2·95	4·90	5·28	5·75

Interpret these results quantitatively in terms of the competing elementary reactions (**31, 32**) of the three pre-equilibrated species, H_2A, HA^- and A^{2-}:

$$H_2A + MnO_4^- \rightarrow \text{products} \quad (1)$$

$$HA^- + MnO_4^- \rightarrow \text{products} \quad (2)$$

$$A^{2-} + MnO_4^- \rightarrow \text{products} \quad (3)$$

The equilibrium constants below apply for $I = 1{\cdot}5$ mol dm^{-3} and 298 K:

$$\frac{a_H[HA^-]}{[H_2A]} = 3{\cdot}5 \times 10^{-2} \text{ mol dm}^{-3}$$

$$\frac{a_H[A^{2-}]}{[H_2A]} = 6{\cdot}0 \times 10^{-6} \text{ mol dm}^{-3}$$

where a_H is the activity of H^+ ions and pH is defined as $-\log_{10} a_H$. Evaluate the corresponding rate constants k_1, k_2 and k_3 for $I = 1{\cdot}5$ mol dm^{-3}.
Source: Simandi, L. I. and Jaky, M. (1973) *Journal of the Chemical Society, Perkin Transactions*, **2**, p. 1856. (Hungary)

Problem 65
The rates of hydrolysis of arylcarbonimidoyl dichlorides ($ArN{=}CCl_2$) in 1:4 dioxan-water solutions have been studied at a temperature of 298 K, at constant ionic strength of 1·0 mol dm^{-3}. The apparent first order rate constant (k_{obs}) defined by $-d[ArN{=}CCl_2]/dt = k_{obs}[ArN{=}CCl_2]$ varied with the pH of the solution as follows for Ar = p-$CH_3C_6H_4$ (I), Ar = C_6H_5 (II) and Ar = p-ClC_6H_4 (III):

		pH				
		2→10	12·0	12·5	13·0	13·3
10^3k_{obs} (s^{-1})	I	3·6	3·9	4·6	6·7	9·7
	II	1·8	2·4	3·6	7·5	13·1
	III	0·46	2·0	5·5	16·1	31·4

Evaluate the rate constants for spontaneous and specific-base catalysed reactions (**32**).

Given the values of the Hammett substituent constants (**28**) $\sigma = -0{\cdot}17$ (p-CH_3) and $\sigma = +0{\cdot}37$ (p-Cl), show that these rate data vary as would be expected if the spontaneous and specific-base catalysed reactions involve the formation of intermediate species of opposite charges in the respective initial steps. (Assume $K_w = 1{\cdot}0 \times 10^{-14}$ mol^2 dm^{-6}.)
Source: Hegarty, A. F. and Dignam, K. J. (1975) *Journal of the Chemical Society, Perkin Transactions*, **2**, p. 1046. (Ireland)

Problem 66

The homogeneous catalysis by potassium ethoxide in ethanol solution of the conversion of the phenylethynylselenoate ions (C^-) into the product 1,3 diselenafulvene derivative (PH) has been studied at a temperature of 305 K. The process is represented stoichiometrically by the equation

$$2C^- + 2H^+ \rightarrow PH$$

The initial rates (R_i) (**4**) of PH formation in the presence of various ethoxide (EtO^-) and C^- concentrations were found to be as follows:

$10^4 R_i$ (mol dm^{-3} min^{-1})	3·63	7·82	17·2	2·57	0·95
$10^3[EtO^-]$ (mol dm^{-3})	1·1	1·1	1·1	3·3	8·9
$10^3[C^-]$ (mol dm^{-3})	0·7	1·3	2·6	1·3	1·3

Use these data to determine whether a general acid (EtOH)-catalysed (**33**) reversible step or a specific acid-catalysed (**32**) reversible step forms the highly-reactive intermediate species, CH, which is considered to react with C^- in a consecutive step (**10**) which is rate-determining for the formation of PH. (The equilibrium $EtOH \rightleftharpoons EtO^- + H^+$ is always maintained).

Source: Ghandehari, M. H., Davalian, D., Yalpani, M. and Partovi, M. H. (1974) *Journal of Organic Chemistry*, **39**, p. 3906. (Iran)

Problem 67

Isopropylidine malonate (IpM) is hydrolysed irreversibly in aqueous solutions to acetone and malonic acid (unity stoichiometry). The apparent first order rate constant (k_{obs}), defined as $-d[IpM]/dt = k_{obs}[IpM]$, in dilute solutions of hydrochloric acid at a temperature of 298 K, varied with $[H^+]$ as follows:

$10^6 k_{obs}$ (s^{-1})	14·31	24·60	36·73	46·92
$[H^+]$ (mol dm^{-3})	0·0999	0·1998	0·3176	0·4165

When IpM was hydrolysed in initially neutral solution, the instantaneous rate of consumption of IpM (R_t) varied with the concentration of IpM consumed (x) and hence reaction time (t) as shown below for a continuous experiment where the initial concentration of IpM was 0·1033 mol dm^{-3} and the temperature was 298 K:

$10^6 R_t$ (mol dm^{-3} s^{-1})	0·356	0·258	0·168	0·109
x (mol dm^{-3})	0·0261	0·0502	0·0699	0·0820
t (min)	1120	2530	4045	5670

Show that all of these results can be explained quantitatively by the same parallel spontaneous and specific-acid catalysed reactions (**32**), evaluating the respective rate constants, and that the hydrolysis in initially neutral solutions shows autocatalysis. Assume that IpM does not dissociate significantly and that all activity coefficients are unity. The malonic acid product maintains a dissociative equilibrium with first dissociation constant $1{\cdot}58 \times 10^{-3}$ mol dm^{-3} and the second insignificant.

(Autocatalysis)

Source: Pihlaja, K. and Seilo, M. (1968) *Acta Chemica Scandanavica*, **22**, p. 3053. (Finland)

Problem 68

The reaction between formaldehyde and benzamide in aqueous solution is first order in each reactant. At a temperature of 333 K and in solutions of constant ionic strength (0·197 mol dm^{-3}), the following values of the second order rate constant, $_2k$, were obtained in buffered solutions of acetic acid (HA) and acetate ion (A^-):

$10^6\,{}_2k$ (dm^3 mol^{-1} s^{-1})	1·95	3·15	4·35	5·55	4·10	4·76	5·44
[A^-] (mol dm^{-3})	0·010	0·040	0·070	0·100	0·050	0·100	0·150
[HA] (mol dm^{-3})	0·010	0·040	0·070	0·100	0·010	0·020	0·030

The concentration dissociation constant of acetic acid is $1{\cdot}57\times10^{-5}$ mol dm^{-3} and the concentration ionic product of water is $9{\cdot}50\times10^{-14}$ mol^2 dm^{-6} under these conditions.

Calculate the rate constants for general acid and general base catalysis (**33**) of the reaction indicated by these results.

Source: Tarvainen, I. and Koskikallio, J. (1970) *Acta Chemica Scandanavica*, **24**, p. 1129. (Finland)

Problem 69

The hydrolysis of N-nitrosohydroxylamine-N-sulphonate (S^-) is catalysed by hydrogen ions and by boric acid (H_3BO_3) with the mechanism

$$S^- + H^+ \underset{}{\overset{K}{\rightleftharpoons}} SH \qquad (1)$$

$$SH + H_2O \xrightarrow{k_2} \text{products} + H^+ \qquad (2)$$

$$SH + H_3BO_3 \xrightarrow{k_3} \text{products} + H_3BO_3 \qquad (3)$$

for pH$\leqslant$8 when borate is present as boric acid.

At a temperature of 288 K and pH=6·80, the half-life ($t_{1/2}$) (**5**) of S^- (determined spectrophotometrically) was 16·0 min and independent of [S^-]. On addition of H_3BO_3 under these conditions, $t_{1/2}$ varied as follows:

$t_{1/2}$ *(min)*	11·9	10·1	8·18	5·84
10^5[H_3BO_3] (mol dm^{-3})	2·64	4·37	7·19	13·1

Show that these results are consistent with the above mechanism (**33**).

A sample of 100 mg of borosilicate glass was digested in $5{\cdot}0\times10^{-2}$ dm^3 of 0·01 M hydrochloric acid, after fusion with sodium carbonate, and the resultant solution was made up to a volume of 0·10 dm^3 with distilled water. To $1{\cdot}0\times10^{-2}$ dm^3 of this solution was added an agent to complex (and render catalytically-inactive) any heavy metal ions and the solution was made up to a volume of $5{\cdot}0\times10^{-2}$ dm^3 with adjustment of the pH to 6·80. When $5{\cdot}0\times10^{-3}$ dm^3 of this solution was added to $1{\cdot}00\times10^{-2}$ dm^3 of S^- solution diluted with $2{\cdot}00\times10^{-2}$ dm^3 of buffer solution (to maintain the pH at 6·80), $t_{1/2}$ was measured as 12·2 min. Calculate the percentage by weight of boron in the glass sample on the basis that H_3BO_3 is the only active catalytic species derived from the glass. (Relative atomic weights: 10·81(B), 1·01(H), 16·00(O).)

Source: Gijsbers, J. C. and Kloosterboer, J. G. (1978) *Analytical Chemistry*, **50**, p. 455. (Netherlands)

Problem 70

The enzyme fumarase (fumarate hydratase) catalyses the interconversion of fumaric acid to L-malic acid in both directions at pH ~7. The progress of the reaction may be followed using the near-ultraviolet (240–280 nm) absorption of fumaric acid. Starting with a solution of one species (either fumarate (F) or L-malate (M)), the initial rates of removal (R_F or R_M respectively) were measured as follows for the same (small) enzyme concentration at a temperature of 298 K:

10^3[F] or [M] (mol dm^{-3})	8·0	4·0	2·0	1·0	0·50	0·25
R_F (arbitrary units)	—	4·414	4·085	3·556	2·824	2·000
R_M (arbitrary units)	4·408	3·724	2·842	1·929	1·174	—

When a solution of L-malate initially was allowed to achieve equilibrium, the concentration of L-malate was 4·6 times that of fumarate.

Evaluate the Michaelis constants (**34**) and the limiting rates under these conditions for the two reactions and show that the kinetic data in combination predict the equilibrium state through the Haldane relationship.

(Haldane relationship)

Source: Nigh, W. G. (1976) *Journal of Chemical Education*, **53**, p. 668. (U.S.A.)

Problem 71

The rate of hydrolysis of phenylphosphate (S) in aqueous solution buffered at pH = 9·2 and at a temperature of 310 K in the presence of the same (very small) concentration of the enzyme known as intestinal alkaline phosphatase has been measured in terms of the initial rate of phenol production (R_i). L-phenylalanine acts as inhibitor (I) (**34**) for this hydrolysis. The variations of R_i with [I] and (S) in these solutions were as follows, with the values shown equal to R_i (μmol min^{-1} dm^{-3}):

[I] (mol dm^{-3})	10^4[S] (mol dm^{-3}) 2·00	1·00	0·667	0·500
0·0000	0·844	0·560	0·420	0·336
0·0028	0·520	0·396	0·320	0·269
0·0150	0·192	0·172	0·156	0·143

Deduce the general type of inhibition involved and evaluate the equilibrium constant(s) for the complex(es) formed with the inhibitor and the value of the Michaelis constant for the uninhibited system.

Source: Ghosh, N. K. and Fishman, W. H. (1966) *Journal of Biological Chemistry*, **241**, p. 2516. (U.S.A.)

Problem 72

The inhibiting effect of metal ions on the rate of lactate dehydrogenase conversion of pyruvate (S) to lactate has been studied at pH = 7·60 and ionic strength 0·1 mol dm^{-3} in triethanolamine-buffered aqueous solutions at a temperature of 310 K. A parameter α was defined as the ratio of rates of the inhibited reaction to the uninhibited reaction under the same conditions.

In the presence of Hg^{2+} ions, α varied with concentrations as follows:

[S] = 2·0 × 10^{-3} mol dm^{-3}			
10^6[Hg^{2+}] (mol dm^{-3})	1·00	1·80	2·50
α	0·793	0·681	0·606

[S] = 4·0 × 10^{-3} mol dm^{-3}			
10^6[Hg^{2+}] (mol dm^{-3})	1·00	1·80	2·50
α	0·882	0·806	0·750

In the presence of Cd^{2+} ions the results were independent of [S] and the variation of α was as follows:

$10^4[Cd^{2+}]$ (mol dm^{-3})	1·00	3·50	5·80	9·30
α	0·979	0·929	0·887	0·831

Deduce the types of inhibition involved for each metal ion and evaluate the Michaelis constant and the inhibitor constants defined as $K_I = [E][I]/[EI]$ or $[ES][I]/[ESI]$, where E denotes the enzyme and I the inhibitor.
(Hint: Deduce expressions for $\alpha/(1-\alpha)$.)
Source: Vanni, A. and Amico, P. (1976) *Annali di Chimica*, **66**, p. 719. (Italy)

Problem 73
A buffered solution of urea ($1{\cdot}50 \times 10^{-2}$ mol dm^{-3}) has been flowed at a volume rate of $4{\cdot}40 \times 10^{-4}$ dm^3 min^{-1} through a cylindrical reactor of constant volume defined by fritted plates and containing 0·200 mg of the enzyme urease (molecular weight = 480 000) immobilised on glass microspheres. The reaction efficiency η was defined as the concentration of urea reacted divided by the initial concentration.

When samples of solutions containing N mols of Hg(II) ions were brought into contact with the immobilised enzyme, all of the Hg(II) was bound to the enzyme. Subsequent passage of the above urea solution showed η decreased (while Hg(II) remained bound to the enzyme) as shown below:

$10^2\eta$	3·300	2·785	2·452	2·072	1·627
$10^9 N$ (mol)	0	0·23	0·38	0·55	0·75

On the basis of plug-flow, a negligible volume of the microspheres compared to the reactor volume and given that the Michaelis constant (**34**) for the immobilised enzyme is very much less than $1{\cdot}5 \times 10^{-2}$ mol dm^{-3}, integrate a differential rate expression to show that a linear relation should exist between η and N for low values of η. Hence evaluate the number of Hg(II) ions which are on average required to deactivate one urease molecule and the rate constant for reaction of the urease-urea complex in the Michaelis-Menten mechanism.
(Immobilised enzymes)

Source: Ogren, L. and Johansson, G. (1978) *Analytica Chimica Acta*, **96**, p. 1. (Sweden)

Problem 74
The rates of methanation of CO_2 or CO (<2% in H_2 in each case) on the same sample of a catalyst of nickel supported on alumina have been measured at a temperature of 500 K and total pressure of 101·3 kPa. The overall reactions are represented by the equations

$$CO_2 + 4H_2 \rightarrow CH_4 + 2H_2O$$

$$CO + 3H_2 \rightarrow CH_4 + H_2O$$

For CO_2 methanation the following observations were made:

(i) Langmuir plots of reciprocal rate versus reciprocal partial pressure of CO_2 were linear with finite intercepts.

(ii) In contact experiments, the fraction of active surface covered by CO_2 was very small (<10%), much less than the fraction covered by H_2.

For CO methanation the observations were:

(i) Plots of $(P_{CO}/R)^{1/2}$ versus P_{CO} were linear, where P_{CO} is the partial pressure of CO and R is the overall rate.

(ii) R went through a maximum value as P_{CO} increased.

Show that these observations are consistent with the identification of rate-determining steps (**35**) as:

(*a*) The adsorption of CO_2 onto the surface in CO_2 methanation.

(*b*) The reaction of adsorbed CO with H_2 adsorbed as such on an adjacent site in CO methanation. (Assume that H_2 is rapidly adsorbed onto the surface.)

Source: van Herwijnen, T., van Doesburg, H. and de Jong, W. A. (1973) *Journal of Catalysis*, **28**, p. 391. (Netherlands)

Problem 75

The rate of dehydration of methanol vapour, represented as:

$$2CH_3OH \rightarrow (CH_3)_2O + H_2O$$

on a polymeric sulphonated styrene-divinylbenzene ion exchange catalyst in particulate form has been found to follow the rate law below in a flow system:

$$-\frac{1}{2}\frac{dn_M}{dt} = \frac{k'P_M}{(1+k''P_M^{1/2})^2}$$

The parameters k' and k'' are constants for a particular temperature, n_M is the number of mols of methanol and P_M is the partial pressure of methanol vapour.

Show that this rate law can be explained by a mechanism where methanol molecules are dissociatively adsorbed (**35**) on two active centres, the rate-determining step is reaction on the surface between the two adsorbed fragments and all active centres are of equivalent activity.

Source: Thanh, L. H., Setinek, K. and Beranek, L. (1972) *Collection of Czechoslovak Chemical Communications*, **37**, p. 3878. (Czechoslovakia)

Problem 76

When CO in O_2 and inert gas (N_2) has been oxidised by passage through a bed of particles of the two solid oxide catalysts specified below, the initial rate of formation of the CO_2 product (R_i) has been measured as below as a function of the partial pressures of CO (P_{CO}) and initially-added CO_2 (P_{CO_2}):

Catalyst A (MnO_2) at 294 K						
R_i (mol s^{-1} (kg catalyst)$^{-1}$)	0·1315	0·1661	0·1848	0·1985	0·1059	0·0939
Catalyst B (35% CuO, 45% ZnO on active alumina) at 429 K						
R_i (mol s^{-1} (kg catalyst)$^{-1}$)	0·2256	0·4475	0·6746	1·1567	0·1964	0·1815
Both catalysts						
10^{-3} P_{CO} (Pa)	5·0	8·0	11·0	18·0	5·0	5·0
10^{-3} P_{CO_2} (Pa)	0	0	0	0	5·0	8·0

In both cases R_i was invariant with the partial pressure of O_2.
Three rate-determining steps are possible:

(*a*) Adsorption of CO onto the catalyst.
(*b*) The surface reaction (**37**) of adsorbed CO and O^{2-} ions on adjacent sites (assuming that surface sites not occupied by adsorbed CO and CO_2 have an O^{2-} available for reaction).
(*c*) The surface reaction between adsorbed CO_3^{2-} complexes and adsorbed CO, assuming that the surface coverage of CO_3^{2-} is directly proportional to that of CO.

On the basis of a Langmuir-Hinshelwood mechanism (**35**), decide which rate-determining step is operating in each case.
Source: Sharma, C. S., Ramachandran, P. A. and Hughes, R. (1976) *Journal of Applied Chemistry and Biotechnology*, **26**, p. 231. (U.K.)

Problem 77
The rate of decomposition of pure nitrous oxide (N_2O) gas has been measured in a stirred-flow (**6**) reactor, where diffusion rates are rapid enough to ensure uniform concentrations of all species throughout the constant volume (V) at the feed rates of N_2O used. A catalyst rack wrapped with gold ribbon of exposed surface area S could be inserted into the reactor so that simultaneous homogeneous and heterogeneous decompositions occurred. Plots of the primary reaction rate per unit volume versus S/V were linear with intercepts (I) on the ordinate and gradients (G), which conformed to the expressions

$$I = \frac{k_A[N_2O]^2}{1 + k_B[N_2O]} \quad \text{and} \quad G = k_C[N_2O]$$

for $[N_2O] \leqslant 7 \times 10^{-3}$ mol dm^{-3} and $S/V \leqslant 15$ dm^{-1}. For temperatures in the range 973 K to 1073 K, the parameters k_A, k_B and k_C depended only on temperature with the variations expressed by the following forms:

$$k_A = 2{\cdot}5 \times 10^{13} \exp(-41\,170 \text{ K}/T) \text{ dm}^3 \text{ mol}^{-1} \text{ s}^{-1}$$

$$k_B = 490 \exp(-14\,300 \text{ K}/T) \text{ dm}^3 \text{ mol}^{-1}$$

$$k_C = 2{\cdot}3 \times 10^4 \exp(-17\,400 \text{ K}/T) \text{ dm s}^{-1}$$

Explain in general terms the origins of the variations of I and G with $[N_2O]$ (**19, 36**). What further information would be required to make a comparison of the Arrhenius activation energies for the true unimolecular activation processes in the gas phase and on the gold surface?
Source: Halladay, J. B. and Mrazek, R. V. (1973) *Journal of Catalysis*, **28**, p. 221. (U.S.A.)

Problem 78
The oxidation of CO by O_2 on a single crystal-face of platinum has been studied by mass spectrometric measurement of the rate of formation (R) of the sole product, CO_2, as a function of time in a continuously-pumped reactor. In one set of experiments at a temperature of 491 K, oxygen at a defined steady pressure (P_{O_2}) was contacted with the surface for a considerable time, before the oxygen flow was cut off and replaced by a flow of CO at a steady pressure (P_{CO}). Measurements were made of the

integrated profile of R versus time, (I), during the very rapid formation of CO_2 and the variation of I with P_{O_2} and P_{CO} was as follows:

Experiment number	1	2	3	4	5
I (arbitrary units)	8·92	8·03	8·03	5·65	3·92
$10^5 P_{CO}$ (Pa)	1·20	1·20	4·30	2·85	1·20
P_{O_2} (arbitrary units)	20·0	10·0	10·0	2·0	0·60

Also the initial R (the maximum value) at constant P_{O_2} was directly proportional to P_{CO} while, on increasing the temperature, I for a specified P_{O_2} decreased.

Interpret these results in terms of an Eley–Rideal mechanism (**37**), involving an initial Langmuir equilibrium (**35**) surface coverage of oxygen, fully dissociated on chemisorption. Determine the value of I (in the arbitrary units used above) at 491 K which would correspond to complete coverage of the surface by oxygen initially.

Source: Bonzel, H. P. and Ku, R. (1972) *Surface Science*, **33**, p. 91. (U.S.A.)

Problem 79

When gas phase mixtures of chlorine and perfluorocyclohexene (C_6F_{10}) were irradiated with light of wavelength 436 nm (only Cl_2 absorbs), $C_6F_{10}Cl_2$ was the only product. Under weak absorption conditions (**38**), initial rates of product formation (R) varied with $[Cl_2]$ and the absorbed light intensity (I_a) as follows but were independent of $[C_6F_{10}]$ at a temperature of 303 K:

Experiment number	1	2	3	4	5
$10^7 R$ (mol dm^{-3} s^{-1})	4·33	12·3	26·5	56·1	39·9
$10^3[Cl_2]$ (mol dm^{-3})	1·90	3·82	6·36	10·5	10·5
$10^9 I_a$ (Einstein dm^{-3} s^{-1})	3·57	7·18	12·0	19·7	10·0

Show by calculation of the quantum yields that these results indicate a chain reaction mechanism. Calculate the kinetic chain length (**14**) in experiment 3.

By devising the photochemical rate law, show that the disproportionation reaction represented by the equation

$$2C_6F_{10}Cl\cdot \rightarrow C_6F_{10} + C_6F_{10}Cl_2$$

must be regarded as overwhelming the combination step

$$Cl\cdot + Cl\cdot \rightarrow Cl_2$$

in chain termination for a four-step mechanism.

Source: Cosa, J. J., Vallana, C. A. and Staricco, E. H. (1969) *Canadian Journal of Chemistry*, **47**, p. 1067. (Argentina)

Problem 80

The mechanism postulated for the photodecomposition (**15**) of methyldiimide (CH_3NNH) vapour by light of wavelength 404·7 nm is as follows:

$$CH_3NNH + h\nu \rightarrow CH_3\cdot + N_2H\cdot \quad (1)$$

$$N_2H\cdot \rightarrow N_2 + H\cdot \quad (2)$$

$$N_2H\cdot + CH_3NNH \rightarrow N_2H_2 + CH_3NN\cdot \quad (3)$$

$$H\cdot + CH_3NNH \rightarrow CH_3NN\cdot + H_2 \quad (4)$$

$$H\cdot + CH_3NNH \rightarrow CH_3NNH_2\cdot \quad (5)$$

$$CH_3NNH_2\cdot + CH_3NNH \rightarrow CH_3NHNH_2 + CH_3NN\cdot \quad (6)$$

$$CH_3\cdot + CH_3NNH \rightarrow CH_3NN\cdot + CH_4 \quad (7)$$

$$CH_3NN\cdot \rightarrow CH_3\cdot + N_2 \quad (8)$$

$$CH_3\cdot + CH_3\cdot \rightarrow C_2H_6 \quad (9)$$

If reaction (7) is very much faster than reaction (9) (in terms of the rates for unity concentrations of reactants), predict the dependence of the overall rate of photodecomposition (**38**) on $[CH_3NNH]$ and on the incident light intensity, under weak absorption conditions.
Source: Vidyarthi, S. K., Willis, C. and Back, R. A. (1976) *Journal of Physical Chemistry*, **80**, p. 559. (Canada)

Problem 81
Deuterium-substituted ethylene is photodissociated by radiation of wavelength 206·2 nm and at a temperature of 298 K in the gas phase the elementary processes involved are as follows:

$$C_2D_4 + h\nu \rightarrow C_2D_2 + D_2 \tag{1}$$

$$C_2D_4 + h\nu \rightarrow C_2D_2 + 2D\cdot \tag{2}$$

$$D\cdot + C_2D_4 \rightarrow C_2D_5\cdot \tag{3}$$

$$C_2D_5\cdot + C_2D_5\cdot \rightarrow C_4D_{10} \tag{4}$$

$$C_2D_5\cdot + C_2D_5\cdot \rightarrow C_2D_6 + C_2D_4 \tag{5}$$

With an initial pressure of 6·65 kPa of pure C_2D_4 in a quartz irradiation cell, after a time of 5 min the following amounts (μmol) of products were detected: D_2 (2·94), C_2D_2 (4·05), C_2D_6 (0·21) and C_4D_{10} (1·37).
(*a*) Derive the ratio of the primary quantum yields (**38**) in processes (1) and (2) and the ratio of the rate constants for reactions (4) and (5).
(*b*) Monosilane (SiH_4) is transparent to 206·2 nm radiation. When SiH_4 was added to the above system, the significant additional reactions (**10**) induced are

$$D\cdot + SiH_4 \rightarrow HD + SiH_3\cdot \tag{6}$$

$$D\cdot + SiH_4 \rightarrow H\cdot + SiH_3D\cdot \tag{7}$$

The isotopic yields of hydrogen formed at 298 K for small extents of reaction in systems with the partial pressures indicated were as below:

$P_{C_2D_4}$ (kPa)	6·72	6·77	6·65	6·70
P_{SiH_4} (kPa)	6·74	2·26	1·36	0·69
D_2 (μmol)	3·14	3·20	3·16	2·91
HD (μmol)	1·13	0·49	0·32	0·16

Evaluate the ratios of the rate constants, k_6/k_3 and k_7/k_6 at 298 K.
Source: Obi, K., Sandhu, H. S., Gunning, H. E. and Strausz, O. P. (1972) *Journal of Physical Chemistry*, **76**, p. 3911. (Canada)

Problem 82
The ultraviolet irradiation of aqueous solutions of pyridine (Pyr) buffered at pH = 8 leads to the overall reaction represented by the equation:

$$\text{Pyridine} + H_2O \xrightarrow{h\nu} H_2N\text{–CH=CH–CH=CH–CHO}$$

with the electronically-excited state of Pyr produced by the primary photochemical act playing the role of a reactive intermediate **(10)** in the overall mechanism. Absorption spectra taken at times after the start of irradiation show the decay of the band due to pyridine at ~250 nm and the growth of the photoproduct band in the vicinity of 350 nm.

Initial rates of product formation (R_i) were determined as a function of the absorbed photon flux (I_a) **(38, 39)**, [Pyr] and [H_2O] (by ethanol addition) as follows:

$10^6 I_a$ (Einsteins dm^{-3} s^{-1})	10·0	6·0	4·3	3·3	3·3
$10^7 R_i$ (dm^3 mol^{-1} s^{-1})	3·00	1·80	0·91	0·70	0·33
10^3[Pyr] (mol dm^{-3})	2·48	2·48	1·24	0·12	0·12
[H_2O] (mol dm^{-3})	55·5	55·5	39·0	39·0	18·5

(The first two systems contain no ethanol.)

Establish the photochemical rate law **(4)**, the quantum yields for product formation, the essential steps of the mechanism and a rate constant ratio for removal of electronically-excited pyridine.

Source: Andre, J. C., Niclause, M., Joussot-Dubien, J. and Deglise, X. (1977) *Journal of Chemical Education*, **54**, p. 387. (France)

Problem 83

When an aqueous solution of ferric perchlorate ($8{\cdot}5 \times 10^{-3}$ mol dm^{-3}) with pH=2·0 (adjusted with perchloric acid) is irradiated at a wavelength of 340 nm, OH· radicals are generated by the primary photoreaction of an $Fe^{3+} \cdot OH^-$ ion pair (formed by hydrolysis) represented as

$$Fe^{3+} \cdot OH^- + h\nu \rightarrow Fe^{2+} + OH\cdot \quad (1)$$

Removal of the OH radical takes place through the competing steps

$$Fe^{2+} + OH\cdot \rightarrow Fe^{3+} \cdot OH^- \quad (2)$$

$$OH\cdot + S \rightarrow \text{inert products} \quad (3)$$

where S represents any species other than Fe^{2+} in the solution and its effective concentration is invariant. [Fe^{2+}] can be measured spectrophotometrically so that the net photoreduction ($Fe^{3+} \rightarrow Fe^{2+}$) quantum yield ϕ_N can be derived.

In a set of experiments with constant incident intensity and a constant irradiation time of 2·5 h **(39)**, Fe^{2+} ions were added initially. The variation of ϕ_N with the average [Fe^{2+}] present was as follows:

$10^2 \phi_N$	7·2	5·0	3·8	2·8
10^5[Fe^{2+}] (mol dm^{-3})	1·8	4·2	6·8	10·4

Show that these results are consistent with the above mechanism **(10)**, where OH· can be considered to be a highly-reactive species, and evaluate the primary quantum yield for process (1). What fraction of OH· reacts in step (2) when the average [Fe^{2+}]=$6{\cdot}8 \times 10^{-5}$ mol dm^{-3}?

Source: David, F. and David, P. G. (1976) *Journal of Physical Chemistry*, **80**, p. 579. (Brazil)

Problem 84

In separate experiments methanol (M) and n-propanol (P) have been photo-oxidised using violet light irradiation of acidic aqueous solutions containing 0·020 mol dm^{-3}

of uranyl (UO_2^{2+}) ions, the absorbing species. The quantum yield (ϕ) for the formation of the keto-product and the fluorescence intensity (I_f) from UO_2^{2+} at around a wavelength of 509 nm were measured as functions of the reactant alcohol concentrations at small conversions and for the same absorbed intensity as follows:

[M] or [P] (mol dm^{-3})	0	0·0050	0·012	0·020	0·035	0·071	0·120
I_f(M) (arbitrary units)	1·00	—	—	0·920	0·868	0·764	0·657
I_f(P) (arbitrary units)	1·00	0·794	0·621	0·495	0·358	—	—
$10^2\phi$ (M)		—	2·48	4·00	6·60	11·8	—
$10^2\phi$ (P)		10·2	19·0	25·2	32·1	—	—

(Letters in brackets denote the alcohol to which the results refer.)

Show that these results accord quantitatively with the mechanism set out below (**10, 39**) (where UO_2^{2+} is denoted by U(VI))

$$U(VI) + h\nu \rightarrow U(VI)^* \quad (1)$$

$$U(VI)^* \rightarrow U(VI) + h\nu \quad (\lambda \sim 509\ nm) \quad (2)$$

$$U(VI)^* \rightarrow U(VI) + heat \quad (3)$$

$$U(VI)^* + R_1R_2CHOH \rightarrow U(V) + R_1R_2\dot{C}OH + H^+ \quad (4)$$

$$2R_1R_2\dot{C}OH \rightarrow R_1R_2CO + R_1R_2CHOH \quad (5)$$

$$2U(V) \rightarrow U(IV) + U(VI) \quad (6)$$

where the alcohols (denoted R_1R_2CHOH) quench the electronically-excited state U(VI)* chemically in step (4) but not physically. Calculate the ratio of the rate constants (k_4) for M and P.

Source: Sakaraba, S. and Matsushima, R. (1970) *Bulletin of the Chemical Society of Japan*, **43**, p. 2359. (Japan)

Problem 85

The γ radiolysis of deaerated liquid acetic acid (CH_3COOH) at a temperature of 298 K, produces the following *G*-values (**40**) for the products: 5·40 (CO_2), 3·90 (CH_4), 0·48 (C_2H_6), 0·22 (CO), 0·45 (CH_3COCH_3), 1·74 ($(CH_2COOH)_2$) and 2·20 ($(CH_3CO)_2$). On the basis that the initial act is ionisation followed by interaction with acetic acid molecules, stoichiometrically represented by the scheme

$$CH_3COOH \rightarrow CH_3COOH^+ + e^-$$
$$\downarrow \qquad\qquad \downarrow$$
$$CH_3COO\cdot \qquad CH_3CO\cdot$$

and that $CH_3\cdot$ radicals are formed by dissociation of these secondary radicals, devise the simplest mechanism which accounts for the formation of the above products. Test this mechanism by equating three appropriate combinations of the *G*-values, individually subject to $\pm 6\%$ experimental error limits. Calculate the fraction of $CH_3CO\cdot$ radicals which dissociate.

Source: Josimovic, L., Teply, J. and Micic, O. I. (1976) *Journal of the Chemical Society, Faraday Transactions I*, **72**, p. 285. (Yugoslavia)

Problem 86

When pure cyclohexane liquid is irradiated with γ radiation, hydrogen is released and cyclohexyl radicals (R·) are formed with $G(\text{R}\cdot)=5{\cdot}7$ (**40**).

When small concentrations of $Cl_2C{=}CClF$ were present in cyclohexane, three derived products were detected, X = RClC=CClF, Y = RFC=CCl_2 and Z = RCl-FCCCl_2H and HCl was formed so that $G(\text{HCl})=G(\text{X})+G(\text{Y})$; bicyclohexyl ($R_2$) and cyclohexene were also formed with yields in the ratio of 1:1·3. At a temperature of 423 K and using small doses so that the fractional changes in [$Cl_2C{=}CClF$] were negligible, the following results were obtained:

10^3[$Cl_2C{=}CClF$] (mol dm^{-3})	G(X)	G(Y)	G(Z)	$G(R_2)$
4·70	9·31	58	61	1·45
9·34	13·8	106	114	1·24
19·0	22·7	184	192	0·88

Devise a mechanism consistent with these results (**14**) and show that an appropriate combination of G(Y), G(Z), $G(R_2)$ and [$Cl_2C{=}CClF$] is constant as demanded by the mechanism.

Source: Horowitz, A., Mey-Marom, A. and Rajbenbach, L. A. (1974) *International Journal of Chemical Kinetics*, **6**, p. 265. (Israel)

Problem 87

$HgCl_2$ is virtually undissociated in aqueous solutions; pulse radiolysis (**41**) results in precipitation of Hg_2Cl_2, following the primary generation of e^-_{aq} (solvated electron), H· and OH· in the pulse. In this system a transient absorption spectrum has been observed in the vicinity of 330 nm wavelength and has been ascribed to the intermediate species HgCl; the half-life of this in its subsequent relatively slow decay was inversely proportional to the dose applied to the system.

For a solution containing $2{\cdot}0\times10^{-4}$ mol dm^{-3} of $HgCl_2$ (argon-saturated to remove air) G(HgCl) was measured as 3·3 and was unaltered when the neutral solution was acidified to pH = 1. When the solution was saturated with N_2O, G(HgCl) fell to 0·6, but when a concentration of 0·10 mol dm^{-3} of isopropanol was added to this N_2O-saturated solution, G(HgCl) rose to 6·1 and the transient build-up was observed to be rather slower than before with the time required for the generation of half the maximum concentration (**5**) being $1{\cdot}7\times10^{-6}$ s.

Interpret these results, taking account of the very rapid processes

$$e^-_{aq}+H_3O^+\rightarrow H\cdot+H_2O$$

$$e^-_{aq}+N_2O(+H^+)\rightarrow N_2+OH\cdot \qquad \text{(independent of pH)}$$

$$e^-_{aq},\ H\cdot,\ OH\cdot+\text{i-}C_3H_7OH\rightarrow \text{i-}C_3H_7O\cdot+\text{unreactive species}$$

Deduce G values for the primary species produced by pulse radiolysis of water.

Source: Nazhat, N. B. and Asmus, K.-D. (1973) *Journal of Physical Chemistry*, **77**, p. 614. (West Germany)

Problem 88

The electrochemical potential (V) (with respect to a standard hydrogen electrode) of an indium (In) anode enriched with the radioisotope ^{114}In and in contact with an indium (In^{3+}) perchlorate solution ($2{\cdot}00\times10^{-4}$ mol dm^{-3}) containing perchloric acid ($3{\cdot}00 \times 10^{-4}$ mol dm^{-3}) has been measured as a function of net current density (i) at a temperature of 293 K as follows:

$-V$ (volts)	0·388	0·365	0·350	0·335
i (A m^{-2})	0	0·590	1·438	3·507

The radioactivity of the solution (I) was found to increase linearly **(42)** with time (t) for a maintained overpotential (η) under conditions where deposition of ^{114}In from solution could be considered negligible compared to its dissolution from the anode. The values of I and t when the overpotential was maintained for a time and then rapidly changed to a new value were as follows:

I (counts s^{-1})	54·0	70·2	113·4	221·3
t (min)	0	50	70	75
η (mV)	0 (0–50)	32 (50–70)	71 (70–75)	

Show that the data from the two sets of experiments are consistent with the anodic process

$$In \rightleftarrows In^{3+} + 3e^-$$

and calculate the value of the exchange current density for the anode, assuming that the symmetry factor is 0·5 and that there is insignificant depletion of ^{114}In in the anode.

Source: Losev, V. V., and Pchel'nikov, A. P. (1970) *Soviet Electrochemistry* (English translation of *Elektrokhimiya)*, **6**, p. 34. (U.S.S.R.)

Problem 89

The electroreduction of dimedone (D) in anhydrous n-butanol on a mercury electrode has been studied, using tetraethylammonium-p-toluene sulphonate as electrolyte. The product was the reduced dimer (HDDH). The potential (V) of the electrode was measured as a function of current density (i) as follows at constant [D] and [H$^+$]:

$-V$ (volts)	1·50	1·58	1·63	1·72	1·87	1·98	$\geqslant$2·10
i (A m^{-2})	10	30	50	100	200	250	290

On the basis of the postulated mechanism **(43)**

$$D_{sol} \rightleftharpoons D_{ads} \quad (1)$$

$$D_{ads} + H^+ + e^- \rightleftharpoons DH_{ads} \quad (2)$$

$$2\,DH_{ads} \rightarrow HDDH \quad (3)$$

(where the subscripts sol and ads indicate species in solution and adsorbed on the electrode surface respectively) determine which species, D_{ads} or DH_{ads} predominantly covers the mercury surface. Calculate values of the surface coverage, θ, on a Langmuir Adsorption Isotherm **(35)** basis for the above set of current densities, on the assumption that only one species is significantly adsorbed, and devise a linear plot to confirm the postulated mechanism.

Source: Kariv, E., Hermolin, J., and Gileadi, E. (1971) *Electrochimica Acta,* **16**, p. 1437. (Israel)

Problem 90

The polarisation characteristics of the evolution of hydrogen at a tungsten-bronze cathode in molar aqueous sulphuric acid at a temperature of 293 K have been measured. The magnitude of the overpotential, $|\eta|$ (mV), varied with the magnitude of the current density, $|i|$ ($A\ m^{-2}$), as follows:

(i) For $|\eta| > 250$ mV, a plot of $|\eta|$ versus $\log_{10}|i|$ was linear with a gradient of ~ 120 mV and back-extrapolation indicated $\log_{10}|i| = -5{\cdot}5$ for $|\eta| = 0$.

(ii) For $50 < |\eta| < 80$, the plot of $|\eta|$ versus $\log_{10}|i|$ was linear with gradient ~ 40 mV and back-extrapolation indicated $\log_{10}|i| = -7{\cdot}8$ for $|\eta| = 0$.

Show that these data are consistent with rate-determining desorption (**43**) of hydrogen atoms as such, when the discharge of protons to yield adsorbed atoms on the cathode surface can be described by the Langmuir Adsorption Isotherm (**35**). Evaluate the exchange current density, $|i_o|$ (**42**) and calculate the fraction of the surface covered by hydrogen atoms, θ, for $|\eta| = 250$ mV and 50 mV.

(Hint: For desorption of hydrogen atoms as the rate-determining step, the current density can be expressed as:

$$|i| = \theta |i_0| \exp\left(\frac{+\beta F|\eta|}{RT}\right)$$

where β, the symmetry factor, can be taken as 0·5).

Source: Vondrak, J. and Balej, J. (1975) *Electrochimica Acta*, **20**, p. 283. (Czechoslovakia)

ANSWERS FOR THE PROBLEMS OF SECTION TWELVE

1. ${}_1k=5{\cdot}08\times10^{-2}$ min^{-1}, $P=76{\cdot}82$ kPa at $t=\infty$, $3{\cdot}0\times10^{-4}$ mols of OAA and CO_2.
2. ${}_2k=14{\cdot}5$ dm^3 mol^{-1} s^{-1}.
3. ${}_2k=0{\cdot}427$ dm^3 mol^{-1} s^{-1}.
4. $t=2{\cdot}6$ s.
5. Orders: 1·5 in $PhN_2^+BF_4^-$;1·0 in H_3PO_4. ${}_{2\cdot5}k=6{\cdot}7$ dm$^{4\cdot5}$ mol$^{-1\cdot5}$ s^{-1}.
6. Order$=3{\cdot}8$. ${}_{3\cdot8}k=5{\cdot}5\times10^{-4}$ dm$^{8\cdot4}$ mol$^{-2\cdot8}$ min^{-1}.
7. First order in NH_2OH, third order in OH^-.
8. Half order in toluene, third order in H_2: ${}_{3\cdot5}k=51{\cdot}1$ dm$^{7\cdot5}$ mol$^{-2\cdot5}$ min^{-1}.
9. Second and third order terms in Im. ${}_3k=0{\cdot}208$ dm^6 mol^{-2} s^{-1}, ${}_4k=2{\cdot}23$ dm^9 mol^{-3} s^{-1} (subscripts indicate overall order).
10. (*a*) 40·1:1; (*b*) ${}_2k=2{\cdot}11\times10^4$ dm^3 mol^{-1} s^{-1}.
11. ${}_2k=5{\cdot}62\times10^4$ dm^3 mol^{-1} s^{-1} in both experiments.
13. $[Cl^-]_o=4{\cdot}42\times10^{-6}$ mol dm^{-3}, ${}_2k=1{\cdot}04\times10^{11}$ dm^3 mol^{-1} s^{-1}.
14. Functions: $(1-P)^{-2}$ for $r=1$, $\ln\left(\frac{r-P}{1-P}\right)-\left(\frac{r-1}{r-P}\right)$ for $r=1$.
15. Termolecular combination: $(CH_3)_2COH^+ + 2$ acetone $\rightarrow$ $((CH_3)_2CO)_2H^+ +$ acetone: $m/e=117$.
16. ${}_1k=9{\cdot}0\times10^{-4}$ min^{-1}.
17. ${}_2k=1{\cdot}2\times10^4$ dm^3 mol^{-1} s^{-1}.
18. ${}_1k(s^{-1})=0{\cdot}057(r=1{\cdot}40)$, 0·076(2·50). 0·107(5·00), homogeneous ${}_1k=0{\cdot}038$ s^{-1}
19. $T=1054$ K, $k_B=7{\cdot}5$ s^{-1}.
20. $E_a=83{\cdot}6$ kJ mol^{-1}.
21. $k_f=3{\cdot}65\times10^{-4}$ s^{-1}, $k_b=9{\cdot}2\times10^{-5}$ s^{-1}.
22. $k_f=4{\cdot}4\times10^{-4}$ dm^3 mol^{-1} min^{-1}, $k_b=2{\cdot}0\times10^{-4}$ dm^3 mol^{-1} min^{-1}.
23. $k_f=5{\cdot}68\times10^5$ dm^3 mol^{-1} s^{-1}, $k_d=17{\cdot}2$ s^{-1}.
24. $k_f=1{\cdot}0\times10^{10}$ dm^3 mol^{-1} s^{-1}, $k_b=1{\cdot}7\times10^5$ s^{-1}.
25. $k_1=7{\cdot}93\times10^{-5}$ s^{-1}, $k_2=5{\cdot}69\times10^{-5}$ s^{-1}.
26. $T=295{\cdot}5$ K.
27. $V(IV)+Cl_2 \rightarrow V(V)+Cl_2^-$ (1), $V(V)+Cl_2^- \rightarrow V(IV)+Cl_2$ (−1), $V(IV)+Cl_2^- \rightarrow V(V)+2Cl^-$ (2), $k_1=27{\cdot}4$ dm^3 mol^{-1} s^{-1}, $k_2/k_{-1}=10{\cdot}5$.
28. $k_1=0{\cdot}19$ dm^3 mol^{-1} s^{-1}, $k_3/k_4=0{\cdot}12$.
29. $D(O—O)\simeq E_1=154{\cdot}4$ kJ mol^{-1}, $E_2=49{\cdot}6$ kJ mol^{-1}.
30. $k_2=1{\cdot}26\times10^{11}$ dm^3 mol^{-1} s^{-1}, collision frequency$=1{\cdot}33\times10^{11}$ dm^3 mol^{-1} s^{-1}.

31. (*a*) ${}_2k=103$ dm^3 mol^{-1} s^{-1}; (*b*) Effective reactions: $Br_2+HCN \rightarrow BrCN+H+Br^-$ (1), $Br_2+CN^- \rightarrow BrCN+Br^-$ (2), $k_1=90$ dm^3 mol^{-1} s^{-1}, $k_2=7{\cdot}1\times 10^9$ dm^3 mol^{-1} s^{-1}.
32. $Tr^-+Py \rightleftharpoons Tr+Py^-$, $Py^-+Py^- \rightarrow Py^- - Py^-$.
33. $k_1=2{\cdot}2\times 10^2$ dm^3 mol^{-1} s^{-1}.
34. Plots (ii) and (iii) are linear.
35. Step (3).
36. Linear chain reaction, $CH_3\cdot$ as chain carrier, order is 1·5.
37. Reaction (5) is dominant.
38. $R_3/R_5=2{\cdot}0$.
39. $k_{24}/k_2=374$, $k_{25}/k_1=75$.
40. $E_a=17{\cdot}9$ kJ mol^{-1}.
41. $k_p/k_d=0{\cdot}28$.
42. Fe_2O_3 lowers E_a for propagation step, increases rate of propagation ($\times$ 3·5 at 323 K), increases rate of initiation/termination ($\times$ 17 at 323 K).
43. $k_p=6{\cdot}46\times 10^{-3}$ dm^3 mol^{-1} s^{-1}, current efficiency = 20%.
44. $\langle k(E)\rangle=3{\cdot}49\times 10^7$ s^{-1}(C), $6{\cdot}18\times 10^7$ s^{-1}(F). $CCl_2\cdot$ not thermalised.
45. $k_5/k_2=0{\cdot}53$.
46. Collision efficiency of He = 0·02.
47. ${}_2k=1{\cdot}3\times 10^{11}$ dm^3 mol^{-1} s^{-1}, collision frequency $=1{\cdot}0\times 10^{11}$ dm^3 mol^{-1} s^{-1}.
48. Estimated rate constant $\sim 3\times 10^{10}$ dm^3 mol^{-1} s^{-1} at 2500 K.
49. ~70% reversion.
50. 0·51 for geminate reactions, 0·044 for geminate disproportionation.
51. $k_1=9{\cdot}8\times 10^9$ dm^3 mol^{-1} s^{-1}, $k_{-1}=1{\cdot}7\times 10^6$ s^{-1}, diffusion-limiting rate constant $=7{\cdot}4\times 10^9$ dm^3 mol^{-1} s^{-1}.
52. For solvents in order given: $5{\cdot}91\times 10^8$, $3{\cdot}76\times 10^8$. $2{\cdot}08\times 10^8$ dm^3 mol^{-1} s^{-1}.
53. $A=10^{14{\cdot}6}$ s^{-1}, $\Delta S^{\ddagger}\simeq +19$ J mol^{-1} K^{-1} suggesting cyclic intermediate.
54. $E_a\simeq 176$ kJ mol^{-1}, $\Delta S^{\ddagger}\simeq -40$ J mol^{-1} K^{-1}; indicates non-dissociative formation of 6-membered, cyclic transition state.
55. $\Delta H^{\ddagger}_f=34{\cdot}6$ kJ mol^{-1}, $\Delta S^{\ddagger}_f=-93{\cdot}9$ J mol^{-1} K^{-1}, $\Delta H^{\ddagger}_b=128$ kJ mol^{-1}, $\Delta S^{\ddagger}_b=-44{\cdot}4$ J mol^{-1} K^{-1}.
56. BCl_3: $A=2{\cdot}2\times 10^8$ dm^3 mol^{-1} s^{-1}, $E_a=107$ kJ mol^{-1}, $\Delta H^{\ddagger}=95$ kJ mol^{-1}, $\Delta S^{\ddagger}=-109$ J mol^{-1} K^{-1}. HBr: $A=3{\cdot}0\times 10^{11}$ dm^3 mol^{-1} s^{-1}, $E_a=162$ kJ mol^{-1}, $\Delta H^{\ddagger}=151$ kJ mol^{-1}, $\Delta S^{\ddagger}=-49$ J mol^{-1} K^{-1}.
57. $\Delta V^{\ddagger}=-3{\cdot}30\times 10^{-5}$ m^3 mol^{-1}, ($\Delta V^{\ddagger}_{\ddagger}\simeq 0$): ‡ has a product-like configuration.
58. $k_f=2{\cdot}9\times 10^7$ dm^3 mol^{-1} s^{-1}: $\Delta V^{\ddagger}=2{\cdot}05\times 10^{-6}$ m^3 mol^{-1}; solvation.
59. $\Delta V^{\ddagger}=1{\cdot}2\times 10^{-5}$ m^3 mol^{-1}, $\Delta\bar{V}=2{\cdot}2\times 10^{-5}$ m^3 mol^{-1}: solvation/charge density effects.
60. $\Delta H^{\ddagger}=60{\cdot}4$ kJ mol^{-1}, $\Delta S^{\ddagger}=+42{\cdot}3$ J mol^{-1} K^{-1}: solvation/charge density effects.
61. $\Delta S^{\ddagger}=+70{\cdot}5$ J mol^{-1} K^{-1}: mechanism B likely, A needs negative $\Delta S^{\ddagger}$.
64. $k_1=1{\cdot}1\times 10^3$ dm^3 mol^{-1} s^{-1}, $k_2=1{\cdot}9\times 10^3$ dm^3 mol^{-1} s^{-1}, $k_3=1{\cdot}0\times 10^3$ dm^3 mol^{-1} s^{-1}.
65. Spontaneous rate constants (s^{-1}): 0·0036 (I), 0·0018 (II), 0·0046 (III); OH^- catalysis rate constants (dm^3 mol^{-1} s^{-1}): 0·031 (I), 0·057 (II), 0·016 (III). Move in opposite directions with change in substituent electrophilic nature.
66. Specific acid catalysis.
67. Spontaneous: $4{\cdot}02\times 10^{-6}$ s^{-1}: Specific acid catalysis: $1{\cdot}03\times 10^{-4}$ dm^3 mol^{-1} s^{-1}.
68. $k_{HA}=3{\cdot}3\times 10^{-5}$ dm^6 mol^{-2} s^{-1}, $k_A=7\times 10^{-6}$ dm^6 mol^{-2} s^{-1}.

69. 3·1% boron.
70. L-malate: $K_m = 1·885$ mol dm^{-3}, $V_{max} = 5·50$. Fumarate: $K_m = 3·452 \times 10^{-4}$ mol dm^{-3}, $V_{max} = 4·76$
71. Uncompetitive: $K_I = 2·3 \times 10^{-3}$ mol dm^{-3}, $K_m = 1·98 \times 10^{-4}$ mol dm^{-3}.
72. Hg^{2+}: competitive, $K_I = 2·00 \times 10^{-7}$ mol dm^{-3}, Cd^{2+}: non-competitive, $K_I = 4·6 \times 10^{-3}$ mol dm^{-3}, $K_m = 1·10 \times 10^{-4}$ mol dm^{-3}.
73. 3·6 Hg(II) ions per urease, rate constant = 530 min^{-1}.
76. Catalyst A: (b), Catalyst B: (c).
77. Homogeneous Lindemann plus heterogeneous (weak adsorption) unimolecular reactions. Require heat of adsorption of N_2O on gold surface.
78. $I = 12·2$.
79. $R \propto [Cl_2] I_a^{1/2}$. Kinetic chain length is 110 in experiment 3.
80. Rate $\propto [CH_3NNH]^{1·5} I_o^{0·5}$.
81. (*a*) $\phi(1)/\phi(2) = 1·86$, $k_4/k_5 = 6·52$; (*b*) $k_6/k_3 = 0·53$, $k_7/k_6 = 0·2$.
82. $R_i = 5·4 \times 10^{-4} I_a [H_2O]$ mol dm^{-3} s^{-1}. Quantum yields (in same order): 0·030, 0·030, 0·021, 0·021, 0·010. Essential steps: Pyr + $h\nu \rightarrow$ Pyr*, Pyr* + $H_2O \rightarrow$ product (1), Pyr* $\rightarrow$ Pyr (2), $k_1/k_2 = 5·4 \times 10^{-4}$ dm^3 mol^{-1}.
83. $\phi_1 = 0·11$, fraction = 0·64.
84. $k_4(M)/k_4(P) = 0·085$.
85. Fraction of $CH_3CO·$ dissociating = 0·043.
86. $(G(Y) + G(Z))/(G(R·)^{1/2}[Cl_2C{=}CClF]) = 2·11 \times 10^4$ dm^3 mol^{-1}.
87. OH· unreactive with $HgCl_2$, i-$C_3H_7O·$ reacts with $HgCl_2$ to yield HgCl with a rate constant of $2·0 \times 10^9$ dm^3 mol^{-1} s^{-1}, Hg_2Cl_2 formed by combination of 2HgCl, $G(e_{aq}^-) = 2·7$, $G(H·) = 0·6$, $G(OH·) = 2·8$.
88. $i_o = 0·151$ A m^{-2}.
89. DH predominantly covers surface, $\theta = 0·19$, 0·32, 0·42, 0·59, 0·83, 0·93 in order given, linear plot of $\ln (i/(1-\theta)^2)$ versus V.
90. $|i_o| = 3·2 \times 10^{-6}$ A m^{-2}, $\theta = 0·99$ (250 mV) and 0·04 (50 mV).

INDEX

The numbers appearing in this index are example numbers rather than page numbers. The numbers in bold type (e.g. **27**) refer to worked examples in sections 1–11, while the numbers in ordinary type refer to exercise problems in section 12.